Can You See What They Do to You?

Can You See What They Do to You?

Chashai

Lee Frank

416 9230898

Please call when you red the book.

VANTAGE PRESS
New York

Published by Vantage Press, Inc.
419 Park Ave. South, New York, NY 10016

Manufactured in the United States of America
ISBN: 0-533-15197-X

Library of Congress Catalog Card No.: 2005902103

0 9 8 7 6 5 4 3 2 1

Contents

Acknowledgments

All my debts go to my Aleph Bet tutors when I was 2 1/2 years old, and onward to my teachers of the Hebrew Prayer Book and the Holy Scriptures. Moses, his pain and humility are a constant example to me. The Baal Tanya, to his son and grandson I owe my adult education, as well as to a chain of medieval teachers of the law—the Torah.

Tom Segew and Joram Hazony I owe for their heart-rending books on contemporary Jewish history.

To a humble poor factory worker. Amram Gaal who kept my spirit up when it was low. I owe what money cannot pay and remains inscribed on the inner walls of my heart. For tho many good suggestions and help I am grateful to my friend D Barecky.

Can You See What They Do to You?

Second Enlightenment: Man Discovers Himself—the Lord—

When he lifts his face toward the Heavens,
he is entranced with what he sees.
Reflected in unlimited possibilities, himself—
And he worships now,
Him, who may be there in Heaven invisible,
but very comprehensible within, and perfect.
For thus knows every man himself and loves Him,
the Lord, himself, he fathoms reflected there
in Heaven and on Earth in himself and in his
     fellowman.

And he also fears Him, that is himself.
His own evil inclination multiplied a million-fold.
For he knows the consequences of wrath,
when unchained—
and is in awe.

Thus doth man contemplate himself
in Heaven and on Earth constantly.
That's how he has come through millennia
and the paths of progress,
out of bondage and oppression
into light and recognition of himself,
into freedom, becoming evermore like Him,
the image he coaxes constantly

1

to rise like tides.

For he fears, with certainty, he knows,
the morrows he remembers possible.
Ah! Even better!—
At the mere thought of love toward himself
in every other man on Earth
from end to end—Lord.
For indeed such is He:
There is no limit to what he can conceive
and translate into reality.
He is creator, Lord.

*   *   *

What is happening though now in our times?!
What happened? The Lord?
Where is the Lord in man?!
My fellowman?!—As if he were vanished
and become invisible,
Man is hidden and it's hard to find him,
as if he became unreal
(he has been banished from within
and is not ruler now).

For indeed, not man,
but Desire rules now.
Desire larger than himself and his ability to be.
(The desire of his imagination,
that blinds the eye and obliterates the vision.)

Desire obliterated now reality,
the Lord, Himself and fellow man.
Man sees now not with his eye

2

but with the imagination of his desires.
He is a captive now,
a slave of his imagination
and of the desire of another Self,
of someone else, "another man,"
another human being,
actually swallowed up, perhaps,
and is inside him devoured,
from which he does, he thinks
grow larger and stronger,
more mighty—almighty!!!
Though in reality, he has just devoured himself.

And as he ceases thus to rule over himself,
man ceased to be Lord,
he just about ceased to be.
His sovereignty and Lordship
that he cannot or will not bear, are obliterated now.
He is neither sovereign nor Lord.
Alas, he is hardly man.
(Should I say he is a cannibal now, a Cain)?
The Lord is now made invisible, residing outside man,
terrible, cruel, and demanding sacrifice.

*   *   *

The spirit that animates the future King
that gives him strength to free man
from his own oppression
and restore reality of the Lord,
the Sovereign the People,
is the spirit of the people.
And as that spirit enters him,
the future king a million-fold multiplied

he too is entranced with what he sees
reflected there,
when he lifts up his face toward the Heavens.

The illusion tantalizes:
Clothed in the glory of majesty,
the People, the Sovereign, the Lord,
Himself.
Yes, all the people's will,
all your desires are all in Him now,
and he shudders.
For he knows as he looks up untoward
the vast immense and empty skies again,
that what the heavens reflect
are mere vastness, vanity and emptiness;
all man's desires (and their inhumanity),
and not at all the Lord.

For the Lord is now invisible.
Thus the ruler begets a terror
for he now knows with certainty,
that what the heavens reflect,
is but himself, the man,
and not at all a God.
What is in him now thus, is mere Desire.
The desire of all the People,
and that is his desire too.
And that Desire is larger than he,
and his ability to endure, The Glory,
and to discharge the service that is Her due.
And this now, awakens a disquiet in him,
in the ruler suddenly.
For as you know yourself:
desire has no limits,

it tolerates no rivals,
and it does not share.
It becomes sheer greed.

An irrepressible lust obsesses the ruler now.
A lust for power and for wealth (for things).
And this your dreadful appetite,
this your spirit,
he breathes back down into the body of the people,
animating you to follow his pursuits.
The ruler it is who corrupts now,
who wakens the greed for power and for wealth
in those next to him,
and further down and deep unto the least and last
little village mayor and policeman.
Thousands of hands does he make rise
toward himself now to support him
and share the glory of his majesty.
The ruler and the people are all one now.
That is how he begets his strength, your ruler,
from the people, from you!
You make him possible:
because you too love it so,
and you are just like he, your ruler is
and those who govern you are.

And in order to achieve this (what I just said above),
the rulers rise on promises.
Promises, i.e., extended hopes.
Promises that they cannot keep,
and on ideas, i.e., incomplete projections of possibilities,
that they know are untrue,
and because you,
who did not heed and made their rise possible.

They only know the power of desire
that's concealed within them,
the power that you the people gave them for their
        promises,
that made them Lords,
and the debits that they failed to discharge
by not serving you.
(And by serving you),
and this frightens them;
for will they be found out?!

As if in a hateful wrath with themselves now,
For not having lived up to the promises made,
to the ideals,
and out of fear of you
(lest they lose the great commission),
your rulers trample you.
That is what makes them such dreadful enemies.
Their fear.
(Each ruler is his own people's most fearful enemy),
(while each one calls the other so).
(Remember: Alexander, Caesar, Genghis Khan,
Napoleon, Stalin, Hitler, Mao,
were mostly killers of their own people.)
This fear pervades them too
the men who rule us now
like a tremor.
A tremor that precedes destruction.
That is why the earth trembles beneath us.
As if the transgressions provoked the wrath of
a force metaphysical that shapes destiny,
the wrath of all the People.
And so he should not betray you,

he will not betray himself.
For you would kill him then,
and get a new ruler instead,
if he deluded you of what you cherished most,
your glory,
the image of yourself in him
(and your paycheques in napalm
and other death factories).

This is the crucial essence of our times:
because this false reality,
of the rulers' illusion of themselves,
have assumed such vast importance (dimensions)
in their own minds and in yours,
as if they were, you, all humanity,
the entire Earth.
As vast as the skies with which they and you
confound reality and yourselves.
For what you worship
is mere glory of majesty.
Yourselves thus tremendously enlarged,
Vanity.
Rulership vastly enlarged and dreadfully destructive.

In both thus, the ruler and yourselves
originate the dreadful character of our times
of man and of the nations.
Because the Sovereignty and Lordship
you now perceive, are not reality,
but the mere magnified reflection
of all your abdicated strength,
and you are trembling.
You are terrified of your own
immensely enlarged mirror image,

that you give now the strength of reality.
For you well know the cost and sacrifice
you require for this enlarged desire,
(war upon your neighbour and all he has),
and you are benumbed utterly and dumbfounded
and stand still now therefore
before your own destroyers.
(You know in war there are no victors, only victims!
You! And them! Both!)
Thus the central point of all happenings now
is what your three big rulers do,
and that is their own desires,
your desires dreadfully enlarged,
they pursue with a dreadful appetite,
at a dreadful cost.
(Bush, Putin, Mao)

*   *   *

The Earth is like a seething pot.
The nations are boiling with anger.
Nation against nation is overflowing with aggression.
Against themselves are the nations boiling with anger,
for being wrathful with other nations.
Against themselves are the nations boiling with anger
for not being wrathful with themselves.
For not being wrathful with their rulers
who enticed them into their wrathfulness,
who lured them to consent,
who make them eat the flesh of victims, just as they do.
Against themselves are the nations boiling with anger
for they loathe themselves,
for being abominable, just as "they," the rulers, are.

Bad conscience agitates the nations,
that makes the Earth now like a seething pot.

*   *   *

Though the Earth is like a garden of Eden.
But because of your rulers,
this garden has become a mourning place,
a place of desolation, a crater,
a volcano top.
And the people?! The people are become like sheep
scattered upon the mountain sides,
tended by unfaithful shepherds.
What do I say?! Shepherds?—Wolves!

Now, how has it become that out of the shepherds
there became wolves who tear at you so merciless?
Those who were charged to free man,
from drudgery and want,
they all betrayed their mission.
They let themselves be blinded
by the glory of majesty.
They betrayed their charges.
None of them brought blessings to you.
From one another the new rulers differ
and from the former kings in attire only.
In wickedness they are all equal.
Alas, they surpass one another.
And just like the kings before them,
our rulers too,
transcending all barriers of ideology and creed,
appropriated to themselves divine attributes.
They practice as if they were gods,
but unlike God, alas—they do not care.

Like the god kings of ancient Sumer and Egypt,
and the pagan emperors of Rome,
do the present-day tyrants too have themselves
worshipped and bowed down to.
(See the huge posters of Mussolini and U.S. presidents,
Stalin, Brezhnev, Mao and the throngs greeting them
        and saluting,)
and just like all the great destroyers of mankind,
the Alexanders, the Caesars, the Napoleons,
those who rule us now trample us
with no consideration.

In the secret of their hearts,
the leaders of the East and West alike
belie you even now.
Each one preaches a belief,
a creed about the mystery of rule and of Lordship,
knowing well that they lie.
There is no mystery.
They do not believe.
They all preach they do
but they don't believe in any creed or ideology.
They are far too clever to suspect them otherwise,
that the way of doing things really makes a difference.
They belie you consciously.

Your shepherds, your unfaithful shepherds,
your scientists, thinkers, and men of letters,
all who are supposed to take care of you
are benumbed from the sheer terror
of their deeds they are aware of,
and the consequences that they well foresee.

They are unable to think,
so dead are they.
They are dead already in advance out of fear.
Your elite has cheated you, causing you to err.
They made you, the Lord, the people invisible.
They wrapped government in mystery,
and uphold it and magnify the mere reflection,
of your mere mirror image, that is not real,
and make you worship them,
and make you tremble and shiver
for fear of indecision.
Whose rule is it now?
You do not know any longer.
What is it that is devastating you so?
Is it your will,
the desire of all of you in your ruler,
or is his will your desire?
This is the dreadful reality,
the meaning of people's government.
All is solid liquid.
You cannot put your finger on it—
is it energy or is it matter?
The "people's" "elected"
"delegates" in "parliament"—
four ambivalent untruths in limbo.
You make atrocious rules against yourselves.
Your rulers merely voice them.
You are bewildered.
(You think now on the parliaments of E&W,
taxes, economic and human sacrifice,
all for their own protection.)
They distract you from peaceful pursuits
with pollution, population explosion,
and depletion of resources, to frighten you.

From everywhere your brother's blood
is crying out—You hide your faces and refuse to see.
Your killer rulers you call fathers,
and the most lethal issues of our times
you call by other names.
And the truth you let to be displaced constantly,
and this is now with you a way of life.
The dilemma has become permanent,
and you cannot tell anymore which is the cause,
and which is the consequence.

As if a punishment from on high,
because he the Lord your real self,
your brother in you, is a burden,
of which you wanted freedom at all cost.
You refused the covenant with the Lord,
with yourself in fellow man,
and you swore allegiance to your ruler instead;
that is why you are no longer sovereign
and have nought left to say in determining
your life, your destiny, your very being.
Alas, you just about aren't.

*   *   *

The knowledge of the death of thousands
that he caused,
rages with terror inside your ruler.
And this terror he extends over you now,
who made this possible, intensified.
And it is your turn to tremble now,
for you permitted it.
And because the dead cannot be revived,

12

therefore, neither can he nor you make good.
Therefore is your tyrant's terror
so very great and terrible,
because the dread that you perceive now,
is dreadful to him equally.
It is the added up terror
that all the victims have endured
and he knows to the minute detail how it was.
Therefore are our times so dreadful
and make no sense.
Even to them who want to rule you all,
and be like God, and own all the earth,
their doings make no sense.

For life itself it seems has ceased to make sense.
For in order to achieve their goals
your three competing tyrants are contesting
their claim to sole lordship now once more,
and in this final contest you too
are required to participate
and offer your very life in sacrifice—
All of you.
They know this, and so do you!
That is what makes you all so dreadfully depressed,
and in turn that is what depresses them.
For whom will they rule then,
when all life from earth is gone?!
Nor can this be changed to any other course,
because, as I repeat, the tyrants know
that they cannot make good,
for they cannot revive those
whom they caused to die.
Only if they could, Oh!
Then they would be Gods . . . !

(At least one of them!
The one with most power,
and least compassion!)
He would be a God!
Can you not see?!
All three of your accursed tyrants dream just that.
How great and well it all will be with thee then,
each one tells you,
if you only made Him Lord!
Perhaps they could cajole you into trying
just a little more. . . . One more hooray. . . .
Just a few more million victims.
Make them Lord! Make them Lord!
Bow down! Bow down, and worship!
They are trying to compel you,
and you do not even see it,
that is just what they are doing now.
That is why all three your devourers
cannot reach accord on anything:
on NATO, disarmament,
the Middle East and the Far East,
and seethe iniquity throughout
the small nations of the globe,
in continuous waves of violence
for expansion and conquest,
all three of them.
And you have lost your minds entirely!
You are benumbed with terror
that is at your doorsteps.
For you know,
it is you now, whom the tyrants mean to kill
and you approve even your own killing.
Your most tender beloved children's
killing you approve.

It is your recklessness, that of all of you,
that has entered your rulers
and pursues the victims now,
that is you, unto your death.
With economic, political and social order
that is unbearable,
that comes back upon you,
and his cruelty, your cruelty,
multiplied is cruel to you now,
threatening your very life.
The victims of your ruler,
your victims,
have multiplied,
and their curse is multiplied
and is now upon you like a cloud.
Both you and your rulers
are hiding behind each other
and behind your own dreadful conscience,
the secret of your enlarged desire you must fight,
for it keeps on "sneaking" in on you all the time.
(Sin coucheth at your doorstep constantly
and hinders you from being.)
It is your ruler's wish, his desires,
that hinder you from being.

Constantly you want to rid your conscience of reality.
All the time you try to hide behind "them"
who govern you, your elite, your parliament,
even behind yourself and your limitations.
"They," anyone . . . just not yourself.
I hear your advocates already
(Solzenitsyn and others)
have begun the wrapping job and their shielding,

excusing and protecting you behind ignorance,
impotence, shifting the blame from you on "them."
("No one knew" the Nazis murdered people.
"No one knew" that Stalin was terrible.)
And no one knows about the terror that is now.
And that one yet in the making.

*   *   *

But I will not permit you this.
I won't let you hide.
I will call up and gather all the millions
that you have tortured and had murdered,
and let them stand before you and frighten you.
Even in your sleep
you shall see their empty eye sockets
stare at you and keep you awake
until the dead stone heart of yours shall wake up too!
Or perish!

*   *   *

—April 23, 2004

I

The
Enlightened
Dark Ages

1

The Enlightened Dark Ages

The rumble comes from the bowels of the earth. From the depths of her throat do the screams of all the victims rise to the skies. In one big roar, 250 years long now.

Ever since the kings were removed from their thrones, the netherworld opened up and swallowed the victims by the millions. And each one of the killers are glorified by all of you, praised and extolled.

*   *   *

So now come with me to this giant cinema and see what they do to you.

*   *   *

The history of mankind is a history of incessant wars, and the rise and fall of empires at the cost of much bloodshed.

Just to mention one before this our enlightened era began, remember what the Spanish and Portuguese white gods did to the Inca, Aztec, population of the newly discovered continents.

*   *   *

At about 1750 lived some very enlightened people—Rousseau, Voltaire, Diderot, Pascal, and so the age was called one of enlightenment. Winds of revolution blew from one end of the earth to the other. New spirits dominated the lands. Liberty, Equality, Fraternity, Democracy.

This was not too long ago. Your ancestors chose men from among themselves and sent them to the old royal palaces where people's democratic governments were formed to be fair and equal to everyone. They were to represent you, the people's will, and voice your desires! The new servants were to stand barefoot with their heads bent before you, the lord, the people. But as you gave up your collective strength to your new rulers, that strength entered them and changed them entirely. This strength gave them the power of malevolent deities and the power to make you obey them and consent. As soon as they established themselves in their cushioned chairs, they differed only in attire from the former kings. In reality they were worse, much worse.

First they drafted a book of laws called the "constitution." That book gave the new elite the power to define law, the rules of justice, to tax, to establish and disestablish rights to property, to define the value of money, and set up a police system to enforce the new rules and to protect themselves.

The new rulers became oligarchies, Danton, Marat, Robespierre, St. Just, have brought terror that was unprecedented in the history of France. The first thing they did was chop off the former king's head, although Louis XVI hardly did any ruling and was no worse than the kings before him. So they did to his queen just because she said, "Let the people eat cake," when she heard they had no bread. They beat to death their seven-year-old little boy who didn't even know that he was to be the future king. Then they did away with the entire propertied class without due process of law, and the river Seine flowed red for a while with the blood of the guillotined. The former owners' wealth the new elite transferred to themselves, their friends and relatives.

Your forefathers were decent people, just as you are now, but they were there at the time of these events and stood by unmoved, just as you are here now, standing by your current tyrant's atrocities and do nothing about it. The intellectuals, scientists and the men of letters who should have been your protectors then, as are their equivalents now, are all traitors. They blindfolded you, the people, and wrapped government in mystery, compelling you to obey. Your treacherous representatives in parliament then and now betrayed you likewise. But the horrors would have never taken place if your rulers did not know that you approved of the murder, rape and plunder that was in your blood just as it was in their own, and that comes with mother's milk. (They came from among you, after all.)

Among the many new atrocities the government ordered was conscription without consulting you, the people, and without your mandate. Your "eyes and your ears" saw well through the book of lawlessness but did not put their foot down to defend you. How was that possible? Was it because the rulers were just like you, the people? Or were you the people just like the new rulers were?!

Thus the men, who were **there** at the time of your forefathers, permitted the government to suddenly make enemies of your neighbours with whom you had lived in peace for centuries and hardly knew one another, and who did no wrong to them. Your forefathers empowered the new rulers to make wars to murder their own sons, fa-

21

thers, brothers and husbands. The entire nation just looked on and did nothing about this. And this goes on to the present day, to our own times.

Your wives and mothers did not bar the gendarmes at the doors who came to abduct their men. They sent them off cheerfully with accolades and song on to those slaughter-fields, because they wanted it, and they knew they wanted it. They began to hate their men, who were like their ruler was. And remember: nothing has changed to date.

*   *   *

The age of industrialization started about the same time as these new dark ages called "enlightenment." The steamship and locomotive were invented and factories were set up for mass production of a variety of goods at low cost that were very profitable for the worker and producer. Especially profitable was to produce goods that destroy themselves in great amounts, that is, war goods. The profits bought beer and useless gadgets. Even your children knew from where their toys and goodies come, the death factories. They were utterly unperturbed. So watch well the evolution of morals in the next two hundred years.

This is how capitalism started. Material profit became the new religion to the big industrialist and the little working man equally. No matter what the cost.

The new insanity was called "economy" and consisted of production, over-production, slow-down, halt. This caused up and down swings of income to the people, with consequent worry and anxiety. Now the governments took it upon themselves to be the people's economic caretakers and providers, and the people loved it. Wars were arranged by mutual consent between your rulers and agreed feigned enemies, to restart their stagnating economies on both sides.

By now what evolved to be the capitalist system and its consequences, consolidated itself to stay. Business is directed by the government, the capitalist bosses, and the banks that create money to finance the game. Initially the system was not perfect, but with time it was fine-tuned so that everyone was sharing it happily. The workers wanted a bigger share of what they thought was so profitable a business, eventually did get their demands, and were cheerfully cooperative with all orchestrated events that were to their benefit. (Forget about socialist nonsense: they wanted exactly the same thing as the capitalists did; they just did not know how to do it, and it cost them thousands of human lives among other damages to themselves mostly.) Finally the socialist idea has slowly simmered down and came to full agreement with the management. That is, the capitalists and the workers agreed fully to the process, so history was progressing and business booming. Your desire for material well-being kept you loyal to your rulers and to the system called "the new economy," no matter what the cost to human lives the last 250 years to the present day. But this war "economy" is absurd. It's a dementia that obsessed the economists and the bankers that war production is most profitable. The world is vast and endlessly needy, desperate for goods, that make equally profits for all, if the "economists" would only redirect industry for peaceful needs. Only the rulers ambitions would be curtailed. Their perverted tyranny would not grow.

*   *   *

Why wars are fought is irrelevant. They are profit-able to all those who are not marched off to be killed. For all the others, wars are very profitable. The workers of the world are united all right, and adore the "new system of insanity" that provides for them so well, and they stand behind and acclaim their rulers. Man never stops to give thought to what happens to those others, who were with him the day before and then fell away from his side, be-cause he is made unconscious participant causing his brother's death.

*　　*　　*

Thus, while the excesses of the French oligarchy were still raging, Great Britain decided to send an army against France out of worry that the new madness does not spread upon them too. The French oligarchs orga-nized an army as well to defend themselves and a most apt commander found for it, a born killer: Napoleon Bonaparte. He led the French in a few victorious battles from which usually half the men never returned. And you (i.e., your grandfathers) worshipped this butcher-in-chief. Before they knew, he did away with the oligarchs themselves and had himself proclaimed First Consul and then Emperor of France. His erstwhile friends and broth-ers, all common thugs, he promoted to generals, marshals and kings over the lands he conquered. The former slo-gans of *liberté*, *égalité*, *fraternité* turned into *pour la patrie*, *la gloire*, and *pour l'empereur*.

Generals appeared out of nowhere and barked orders from the top down. Your grandfathers dressed up as sol-diers, obeyed like sheep. Sheep armed with rifles and bayonettes. They were ordered to assault huge numbers of other sheep equally equipped. These sheep suddenly all turned into wolves, assaulting one another with murderous ferocity. They went wild! They could not recognize themselves. And so they came down to our present time, as you consent to your present rulers' command, no matter what they tell you to do.

The maimed and dying men's cries on the battlefields reached the heavens, but not your heart or ears. You no longer hear, no longer see, and no longer feel the others' pain. Compassion is gone out of you, because of greed. Your grandfathers became accomplices to their rulers who had them by their throat, for they knew they all wanted the same thing, material wealth that gives you a sense of power. Ever since, they wear collars around their necks just as you do today. That has come to be because of your consent to all I described above, starting with the revolt against the kings and the ruling class of the time.

After he caused the death of about half the male population of France and a proportionate number of her manufactured enemies across Europe, the little psychopath had outdone his ambition, and his excursion to Moscow and back finished him cold.

You continue to worship the scoundrel. You kneel at Napoleon's tomb in the Invalides for all the good things that came to you through him. Your brothers, killed on the battlefields, you repay with one minute of silence once a year.—That is all.

*　　*　　*

The American Uncivil War

Around the time of the French Revolution, the Americans, too, revolted against the British and produced a civil war. (How a war can be civil is beyond me.) The founding fathers of America, Washington, Jefferson, the Adamses, Hamilton and honest Abe Lincoln, too, wrote a book second only to the Bible, another Constitution.

Armed with this new book in one hand and a rifle in the other, they induced the people to some uncivil warring among themselves, and, at the same time, exterminated the original native owners of the land. Sixty million Indians in all—men, women, children, naked, unarmed and innocent—were slaughtered. This was some "genocide" (the word was not coined yet at the time) and equalled ten genocides of the Jews one hundred years later. As recently as 1905 it was still fashionable on Sundays to "flush out" Beothuk Indians from their wigwams naked, and shoot them like rabbits in hunting parties in the snow.

Can you see the grandiose mansions with chamber music and the candlelit dining halls? The gentlemen just returning from "the hunting party," the ladies dressed in silk. Even the music of Handel and Mozart could not drown out the cry of a black servant being lashed for dropping a spoon or a dish. And these were "ladies and gentlemen."

With the Napoleonic wars finished and the American Civil War over, an **anxiety** about a new economic crisis beset Europe and America in the 19th century. A new insanity called the wars of national liberation began thus as a excuse to regain "economic well-being." (Independent nations and states are a relatively new invention—and they really serve their own purpose solely.)

Nations lived peacefully side by side for centuries, hardly realizing their neighbours were different in any way. Romantic demagogues stirred up a new enmity among these peaceful people and ignited a new round of wars, keeping all the factories humming and filling the pockets with wages for quite a while nearly to the end of the century.

*   *   *

On Belgium

There was a little nation of barely six million Belgians, best known for their chocolates and an imposing king, Leopold II, with an impressive patriarchal beard. This king and his people decided to invade a huge central African territory, the Congo, and rob it of all it had; rubber, tin, gold and elephant tusks. This task was given to native children and adults who were simply kidnapped from their villages and enslaved. Every little slave had a basket to fill by evening, and those who did not meet the quota had their hands chopped off by their overseers and were left to bleed to death overnight. Ten million young native children bled to death between 1895 and 1905.

His Majesty Leopold II laughed heartily with his visitor, the Sultan of Turkey, about how the victims cried, especially the female children, how they shrieked all night until they sighed their last. Their majesties roared loud and were vulgarly amused. They were not demented. But the courtiers who were serving them the champagnes and aperitifs were so, because not one of them had the humanity to kill the amused majesties. No one flinched. No one protested. No one even objected that this was dreadful, inhumane and wrong. Just how cheap human life had become.

*   *   *

On Emancipation

Man's dream now about his strength that once made
him king is but a dream. For his strength, yours and all
others', is now united in your rulers, who exercise cruelty
and deaden you.

Ever since the great verities of life and of morality
were betrayed, discontent, anger and anxiety fill the
heart as it views the scene around itself. Man is desperate
and depressed, for such is the situation now, and he can
do nothing about it, for he knows that he is accomplice to
the ruler and the times. He is longing, therefore, to be free
again as he was before, strong, powerful, sovereign, King.
A thing so indispensable for him in order to be Man, dispenser of all the good things of life. Himself, Creator,
Lord. For how else can he be Man unless he is like God?
And since because of his transgression that has become
impossible, he has withdrawn. Man has withdrawn into
his home and away from public politics in the attempt to
assert his rule there.

Ah! But the house that man lives in now is divided by
the emancipated woman. No! She does not live with him,
but beside him. With an all-knowing arrogance, she con-
tests his domain and denies him sole possession. She
questions his wisdom and causes him to be uncertain
about his abilities. She challenges his pride and provokes
his wrath constantly. Even in the very recesses of the bed-
room she but excites him, frustrates him and gives him no
rest. That is why sex has become such a public preoccupa-
tion in our time. She makes the earth tremble beneath

him with anger. He is losing his mind, the once king, wanders around his own lost life, for he is defeated, he is depressed, he is dead.

Yet this has not been always so. Because of your rulers' bottomless greed that you share, it is that you abdicated your right to be sole provider of all good things of life, and you let your wife be provider too. Because your greed for things that you mostly do not need is larger than your ability to provide, you let your woman in to share what has become a burden now. Your wife detests you for letting her be drafted into the workforce, where she fornicates in broad daylight right in front of you, while you are looking on, unable to stop her, and don't utter a sound. You are no longer king. The constant war is on in your own house now. You are lobotomized and castrated, impotent and incapable of thought, and have no authority. Therefore are the outrages of your ruler all around you. You abdicated the prerogative to be the sole lord from whom all good things of life proceed. She is your ruler's ally now, your wife, and **his** helping mate **against** you. For she is fired now by the same fire, by the self-same desire as you are—a desire for senseless things. She is prodding you and exhausting you constantly and exasperating you with demands you cannot meet.

Thus the ruler got you both precisely where he wanted—really busy with no time to think about what he does so as not to endanger him, and the government can carry on with every perversion and tell you to approve and acclaim, and you all do.

Every empire of the past, Babylon, Greece, Rome stumbled and fell preceded by the dissolution of sexual morality. That weakens the family structure of the empire, which is its building block. Now just look around yourself and see how things are at home and in public. The picture does not promise to last.

What divine retribution! Would you have ever thought of it, that she, your most trusted spouse, would be this treacherous? She is a constant witness to your conscience. Your most guarded secrets she knows (and you know that she knows). Your tyrant's cruelty you help him exercise. Both your wife and children know that you do not hear the cries of your fellow men that rend the skies, because of you. They know you have not protested meaningfully, genuinely against the outrages against the mass murders and holocausts! That is why your own children and your wife look down on you, fear you and hate you. Life became corrupted with the "living standard." The luxuries—cars, motorcycles, bicycles and other needless toys—you are cowardly to give up for the sake of pride and domestic peace.

Industrialization changed you. It harnessed you to an assembly line, a production belt to run on. You don't walk anymore, you only run. Most things made now are for the eye to covet, to want, not for a real need.

I don't deny the value of modernity, but we pay far too high a price for "living." Our modern industrial production is not economical. It's a great burden, that is construed so that we don't notice. It does not make us free. It enslaves us. The new economists have not figured out yet what it takes for an economy to be efficient and profitable, without the cost we pay for it at present. They made you enroll, enslaved even your wife into the workforce. If industrialization was efficient, you wouldn't have to do that. Expenditures for useless things increased and even the two-income family still has not improved their well-being much because all the earnings are spent.

Emancipation is a curse upon your family brought upon you by your rulers.

*　　*　　*

Any barrier to your will is an intolerable irritant that angers you. Man is not tolerant. For this, man resembles God most perfectly just as he is best described. He too feels all powerful, very jealous of his possessions, full of wrath with his contenders, and constantly does he wish to be loved. Thus only can he be constantly gratified and good. That is how God and man most resemble one another. And this circle of action is not to be breached by an equal force at home. Such a thing is alien to man's character, which should permit the same prerogatives for your mate as are reserved for you only. This is alien in nature throughout, where even the moon is made smaller than the sun and made to shine less splendid.

There is no room for equals in man's home.

The writers of ethics, the philosophers, psychologists, sociologists and other so-called preachers, prophets and liars of modern times persuasively soothe you with sayings. They force you to swallow your pride, cultivate manners and **pretend**. In unctuous voices they whisper, "be civilized." Be happy, compromise, be someone else! That's why, in order to survive the hidden torments of your life in compliance with the code of appearances and certified falsehoods, you learn to put on a show nowadays, and try to be all that you are not. You try to achieve substitutes for the real life you have lost, and that you so much want. You are beside yourself, and you hate the stranger that is within you now. The one that you pretend to be, but that you wish you were not. You wish, therefore, anything, anything, even that you may altogether cease to be.

We are beside ourselves. That makes us agitated, for what we live is a substitute, an ersatz existence. Not our real life. The cowardice that made us not rise against our government's misdeeds, our children and our wives and inner circle know. They cannot respect such weak, perverse character. We now make up a society of cowards.

It is our government that has poisoned, polluted and turned our sons and daughters against us, to disobedience and rebellion, corrupting them with sex and drugs. It is the government that weakens us and leaves us without will. The school system in the East and West is for training future armies of servants and sheep. When considering our achievements, measure them up against our happiness.

We must love our children. So they will come back to us and be one with us. So they'll be our strength and consolation, we will recognize ourselves in one another, and we will be one again. We will become **Men** again.

Depression causes you to become indolent even to the most essential problems that affect your life. This is why you don't react to your government's misdeeds that brought you under the shadow of the mushroom cloud. This is why it's possible to commit inhuman atrocities of global scale, and why our times are of crisis in spite of all technological and intellectual advances.

Not until you recognize the oppression you endure at home as the underlying cause of your misery, will you have the courage to admit your indifference to life and to your government's misrule. You will dispel then, this bad dream of pretense and make-believe, and become free and strong again. You will be king at home, and dispenser of all the good things of life again and friendly to your fellow man. Thus will you regain your strength and remove the brutes that oppress you and the entire globe with bloodshed and perversions that rule over human behavior that accepts Lenins, Stalins, Hitlers, Maos, and all the lesser but equally brutal exterminators of mankind in our time.

*   *   *

Origins and Preparation of World War I

Wealth and poverty, aside from being real, begin first in man's mind. An anxiety over the possibility of unemployment, not real diminished income, took hold of man in 1905. Not the prospect of poverty. For most men were much better off than their fathers or grandfathers before them. The anxiety rises and people worry that they will not be able to buy all the useless things they don't need. The big financiers realize this, and they know that the factory worker is as greedy as themselves, so they create a strong desire for work, to be employed to have undiminished income. A desire for money in the mind of the average man is as big as in the capitalists' minds and is insatiable. Money makes both of them feel powerful. The feeling that makes him feel most manly.

Thus plans for a new war were construed in 1914.

The Hapsburg heir to the throne, Archduke Ferdinand and his fiancée were brought to Sarajevo and duly murdered by a prearranged "mad Serb," and WW I started. The intellectuals, thinkers, writers and artists on both sides of the future "enemies" should have known better and protected you from this bloodshed, but they did not. All of them enthusiastically endorsed the war. The foremost minds of Europe, like Freud, G.B. Shaw, and

H.G. Wells, clamoured that this war was a must. "The European mind is 'stagnating' and 'needs to be refreshed,' and 'purged with an ample blood-letting,' " they cheered in unison. (This was also to be the war that would end all future wars.) That little purge cost 25 million lives and countless others maimed for life. There were single battles like Verdun, Somme, Ypres, Marne and Gallipoli that cost a million lives each.

*   *   *

In 1915 it was fashionable in the salons of London and Paris to wear a fez and belong to the "young Turks." Kemal Ataturk, who overthrew the aging, degenerate sultan, had dragged two million innocent Armenian men, women and children from village to village, accompanied by gendarmes on horseback and had them bayonetted, raped, and disemboweled in broad daylight. All in 40 days, and no one protested. King George, the Kaiser, Lloyd George and Clemenceau did not even raise a whisper. Nor did your forefathers, **the people** of that time, say a word on behalf of their fellow men, the Armenians. The "young Turks" were in vogue.

*   *   *

In 1917, in the midst of a still-raging war, the Marxist brotherhood was headed by two psychopaths. Two demagogues on a power trip, Lenin and Trotsky, who outstripped the brutality of Gengis Khan and Attilla the Hun. They promised to introduce socialism and progress into their poor country called Russia. Lenin managed to persuade two thousand drunk sailors on a Kronstadt boat to come with him and lay siege and disperse the Russian parliament, the Duma. He dressed these sailors in impressive long leather coats with boots and revolvers and gave them unlimited authority to act as "People's Commissars" and do the "people's" will.

As their first act, these new commissars murdered the czar and his entire family, children and all.

Then, with these two thousand thugs, the two psychopaths managed to overthrow a country of 160 million people that stretched from the Baltic to the China Sea, while involved in a raging war in Europe. They converted Russia to a Bolshevik Republic, and renamed the land the Soviet Union of People's Republics, the USSR.

I repeat, by the time their successor, the beloved Batyushka Stalin, finished "progressing" and socializing the poor country, he had murdered millions of his own people. And half of that country's inhabitants looked on with no protest as the other half were sent off to the gulags and other extermination camps, never to be seen again. Did you hear the Russians protesting and crying for their near kin? No! No one cared. No one cared.

The Americans helped a great deal to establish this new regime. The Americans were quite eager for communism to succeed. They helped with loans and material support. Herbert Hoover, the Chase-Manhattan's Rockerfellers, J. P. Morgan, Armand Hammer, Harriman and Warburg all helped. For is there a better business than one when you create enemies and finance both sides? They sent an emissary to explore and report on Stalin and the USSR, and the messenger came back, enthused: "I went to visit and I saw the future."

*   *   *

World War I ended. Everyone cheered, but the wid-

35

ows and orphans cheered less. The booming profits from that war eventually were running out again, once more on useless and senseless spending, and a new crisis was emerging again. Do not misunderstand me, I should be more careful as I say it again: It was not a real crisis, but the imagination of an oncoming financial crisis made the situation seem threatening and anxiety producing.

*   *   *

Preamble to World War II

While the future of Europe was being prepared during the 30s, the Japanese decided to conquer Manchuria. In the process, they killed 30 million people. Did you hear what I just said? Thirty million men, women and children, more than the entire human cost of World War I. In order to enhance their troops' morale, the Japanese imperial command decreed a three-day, free-for-all massacre of Nanking. Three hundred thousand innocent civilian men, women and children were killed in **72 hours**. There was a League of Nations that sent Japan a reprimand. The Japanese had a big laugh, then threw the letter into the wastebasket. How mankind from around the globe looked at the gory pictures in the daily papers is beyond me. How spiritual and religious men, Nobel-Prize winners, cultured and learned intellectuals looked on at all this without protest, I fail to understand.

*   *   *

Also Italy attacked Ethiopia with tanks, planes and modern weaponry, while the Ethiopians fought back with spears, bows and arrows before being minced into hamburger meat by the Italian armoured troops. The Italians also laughed when they got a letter of reprimand from the League of Nations. After Ethiopia, the Duce marched over Somalia, Eritrea, Tunis and Libya because they were all savage and needed to be "civilized."

*   *   *

As I already mentioned, the period of 1929–39 was once again a time of economic slowdown. Four-fifths of the world was starving amidst abundance and plenty. The new enlightened thinkers, the new global industry and the agricultural revolution could have provided a good life for all, but the crisis was intensified by the financial rulers and their "economic experts" for the purpose of creating a new war, as war enhances "business" most wonderfully.

*   *   *

Well, to prepare a large-scale war, "preparations" are needed, and so the ruling business circles, who rule the government as well, staged the necessary preparations "properly."

*   *   *

Now, Lo and behold! A veritable miracle! A redeemer. A Lord-sent wonder-boy appeared out of nowhere. A. H. Schickelgruber, "a man of destiny," a semi-literate corporal. A fascinating orator, wild gesticulator who electrified the masses, built up in a short time a sizable following in Germany. His book Mein Krach (I mean Mein Kampf) convinced all who wanted to hear it. "Europe's economic

37

problems are caused by the world Jewish bankers and bloodsuckers, and all the Jews should therefore be killed. We must exterminate the vermin that pollute the earth and cause all its ills. We must **cleanse** Europe and make it **Judenrein.**" (It's also said that the book was ghostwritten for Hitler in G. B. by a man called Hanshoffer?)

Thus the National Socialist Workers' Party was born at a Munich beer parlor. Adolf was the man of choice, of course, sent by Providence! At a later and bigger rally at Nuremberg, the masses all roared Kanonen! At the question, what the people wanted, the answer was Kanonen! Not butter! Hitler was elected as the Fuhrer of Germany, and in no time he annexed Austria to the Deutches Reich before swallowing up Czechoslovakia with the tacit consent of Great Britain and France.

By 1936, the Americans and British had helped re-arm Germany to the teeth. Roosevelt and Churchill gave this wonder boy iron-clad assurances "not to worry." "Even if Germany should be ausplaniert (flattened to the ground), they would rebuild his Reich anew to last a thousand years."

"Ady, mein boy, you make sure to kill those vermin that infest humanity and make Europe Judenrein, and do away with as many Poles and Slavs as you can at the same time, because they're all commies and a menace to humanity." Ach! What a business that will be! What a boom! Well, this will definitely be a lifesaver. The new redeemer eventually arranged a devastation that even God could not do any worse. The Jews were a mere side dish in the whole show. Europe became ausplaniert[*]!!

*Flattened

38

*   *   *

In September 1939, in a small town called Gleiwitz, an "incident was arranged" to make the pretext for war (just as it had been in Sarajevo to start World War I), and the "march nach Osten" began. The Grofatz[*] was very successful when it came to murdering the unarmed populace, but when it came to military matters, he was a mere corporal and no more. He made the blitzkrieg on Poland an unparalleled success. With his tanks and armour he ran over the Polish cavalry that still operated on horses, and in a few days conquered Poland. He killed the seven million unarmed Jews in the process—later called the Holocaust—but by the time he had retreated to his bunker in Berlin from Moscow, this conflagration had cost **70 million** non-Jews. That is ten gentiles for every Jew killed. This was a very expensive and uneconomical war!

The war ended as planned and foreseen. Poor Ady, of course, was not much of a Fuhrer in the end, so he shot his wife Eva and their dog Blondie, and then himself.

Your thinkers and scientists did not protect you from your rulers this time either. The people were drunk with lust for "Macht and Kraft durch Freude," for blood and rape, and the neighbour's wife and property. How did this become possible? What spirit entered you? Was it your ruler's treacherous spirit, or was it your spirit that you vested into him that made you both this perverse and atrocious?

This economy-boosting war ended. The two leading "enemy" leaders, Eisenhower and Erhardt, shook hands for a photo-op in front of a big palace, and behind closed

*Greatest Leader of all time

doors a minute of silence was held undoubtedly for A. H., I would like to presume, before they hugged one another. The Marshall Plan was launched into full swing. Now this was where the *real big money* was made for the next several decades, because Germany had been demolished entirely and needed reconstruction. So the former enemies rebuilt it brand new and gleaming, just as Roosevelt and Churchill had promised they would.

First the German autobahn was built for the late Fuhrer's Volkswagen, for the German Volks. Then they made the Wohnugsvelle, Fressvelle, the Reiswelle, then the Kurwelle, and then the Whorewelle. President Kennedy called out loud and clear during the Berlin crisis in 1961 that nearly wound up in a nuclear war between the former allies, "Ich bin ein Berliner" and was willing to risk one hundred million American lives (and more!) for "the principle America" to prevail, and assured the Germans that America is loyal to them, as promised by Roosevelt and Churchill for the sacrifice the German people made to produce this economic miracle called war and post-war economic recovery. No country became as wealthy after the "lost war" as the fuhrer's Reich, which the victorious allies promised to him in advance.

The heirs of Goering, Himmler, Borman and Mengele visited each other's estates in their Ferraris. Even their grandchildren knew from where the wealth came and so did their schoolmates and neighbours. They all laughed cheerfully, ate, drank, made love. Bad conscience?! What bad conscience?! Repentance?! What repentance?! Thus had the new morality spread—worldwide.

The profitability and economic well-being due to war was thoroughly understood by then. After World War II, the economy went through the roof in Europe and the

U.S. From 1945 to 2000, the New York Stock Exchange, DJIND index went from 140 to 12,000.

Well, do you know at what cost? Five hundred million victims, mostly civilian, mostly women and children, murdered for profit by all the united workers' brotherhood of the world in the death factories **after** the great World War II.

*   *   *

Also let's not forget the Japanese medical experiments on live human beings and Hiroshima while we are on the topic of the last world war. The Korean and Vietnamese wars made the Americans rich and wealthy, obese and obscene. The ten-year war between Iran and Iraq cost 10 million lives. Both sides were armed and supplied by the Americans on credit at no interest.

*   *   *

The former British and French empires, so great for 300 years, and in whose confines the sun never set, dissolved like salt in a water glass in a short span of ten years: 1948–58. Say now, has such a thing ever happened that empires so great vanish so quickly?

USA and USSR were now the new superpowers. They decided for a long, **cold** war on a global scale. It was called so because the principal actors did not engage in active fighting but arranged instead each for their own protéges, proxies, to fight one another on their behalf. Those they supplied with weaponry and all the needs for mutual extermination for free or a mere pittance. The profit came back to everyone working in the factories that produced death for millions across the globe. To keep everyone happy, the world was flooded with opiates, and every destroyer had amplifiers teaching hate all around the world.

*　　*　　*

With American help, Russia (now the USSR) became a great military power, but the line-ups for bread and potatoes were interminable. And the famine killed millions in spite of all the help. We know now the details of the communist enterprise in Russia, but its 85 million victims found out too late. The Communists spread their message worldwide as well, killing millions of people in each country they set foot in. And, for all the victims, no one demanded accounts, no regrets. In Dostoyevsky's *Crime and Punishment*, Raskolnikov torments himself over why he killed **one** innocent woman for no reason. But at page 800 he repents in sorrow, goes to the police station and surrenders for his crime.

By the way, do you know what happened to all the executioners and commissars, CEKA, GPU, KGB, NKVD? **Not a thing.** Many are still alive on big government pensions, in dachas and specially secluded elegant quarters. They do not stand in queues for anything. The best food and drinks are delivered to their home at reduced prices. Their children and grandchildren are front-row candidates for university education irrespective of their IQs, and the best government jobs are reserved for them. Thus the new oligarchy has become hereditary and flourishes.

*　　*　　*

A civil war raged in China between 1940 and 1950 that cost millions of lives, and at the end the winner was the Great Helmsman who devoured China. As soon as he settled with his cohorts in the imperial palace of heavenly peace, he had, by a simple edict, executed 67 million of **his own** people that equaled ten Jewish Holocausts (the term was not coined yet). That was ten percent of all living Chinese then. He had them murdered so he would be feared and obeyed. This new great Chinese people's emperor without a crown, in a bluish grey quilted tunic lived in opulence much more elaborate than his imperial predecessors. And his cruelty was far worse than any of the Chinese emperors of the past.

What did you writers, thinkers, intellectuals and academics of the 650 million decent Chinese people do? What paralyzed you in front of one tyrant and a few of his cohorts, all former thugs whom the big dictator now named ministers and generals? He himself, the great helmsman, is nothing without you. He is nothing without your collective abdicated strength that makes him so powerful. Powerful!? Almighty!? The Chinese nation multiplied since then to become 1.2 billion, but the great helmsman and sexual pervert had by now about two hundred million of his own people killed. The nation worshipped their devourer and continue adore him to the present day. It is year 2003.

*　　*　　*

(**For the sins of Edom, for the sins of Moab, Kedma, Ammon*** was the biblical prophet preoccupied.) I am just translating to the contemporary: for the sins of causing countless dead of the Napoleonic wars, for the

*The names of biblical countries.

sins of the 60 million Indians killed, for the sins of the Belgians who killed 10 million children in the Congo, for the sins of World War I, with twenty-five million dead and countless maimed, for the sins of two million innocent Armenian civilians butchered during that very war, for the sins of the Japanese in Manchuria that caused thirty million to die, for the sins of the Italians in Ethiopia and all of North Africa, for the sins of the 70 million victims in World War II, caused by the Germans,—or should I just call a spade a spade and spell it outright, WW II caused by the USA and GB. Plus the sin of murdering my seven million holy Jewish brethren. For the sins of Biafra—3 million in 3 months, Indonesia—5 million in 9 months, Bangladesh—3 million in 3 months. Cambodia: half of the entire nation was murdered **by their own sons that the Chinese trained for this purpose.** For the sins of the Chinese rulers who murdered 220 million of their own people. For the sins of Uganda, and several African wars that cost millions of innocent civilians: Algiers, Ethiopia, Eritrea, Somalia and Sudan. I cannot enumerate them all. The latest tragedy being the Burundi genocide, 2 million in two months. And, right now the Congo is fighting a civil war that has already claimed three million dead, and so is Sudan.

For all of these I enumerated and for all those I failed to count a punishment should come upon mankind in a measure equal to this to bring justice upon the perpetrators and right the wrongs that the poor victims suffered.

Did I say 500 million more victims should meet those other victims' end?! Did I just say this?! Or am I out of my mind?! How am I and you to bear the cries of the next 500 million souls whose pain will rend the heavens? The cry of those that are now united in one dreadful roar at the Van Allen Belt deafen us to all reason and won't let us think straight any longer! Lord God! My fellow men! What will happen when the next wave of pain and screams add up? Will You be able to stand that dreadful sound?! Isn't there another way for transgressors to redeem themselves, to make good, and make the pain cease right now?! Isn't there a way to teach mercy, compassion, and a way to right wrongs?! I would like to pray, but I am numb, speechless, not a word comes out of me. I am unable to pray. I will not pray! Lord, show Your mercy now! Show Your compassion and a new way now with no delay.

*   *   *

The Present
(the next ten pages were written between 1950 and 1990)

The burden is hard to bear. The situation is terrifying. The decisions about our fate are just about beyond control and in the hands of evil servants. An evil spirit possesses them and they do not even know it. The victims have accursed you who govern the East and the West alike, and the guilt your bear distorts your vision like a magic looking-glass, that makes you see things differently, be distrustful of one another and unable to compromise.

A psychosis has set upon you again, similar to the ones mankind suffered in the past just before its civilization was destroyed. Then, too, the real battles were preceded by verbal ones, by philosophic crises, when all faith was lost in established values. Crises like the one we are in now. An anxiety, an acute depression has overwhelmed you, both in the East and the West, because you discov-

45

ered that your governments were unfaithful. An anxiety true of all times of upheaval that antecede great devastations. It is like discovering your wife, in whom you laid all trust, to be unfaithful—she must go. Yet the days until she leaves are ones of disorder and bewilderment in the home where there is none other to substitute her yet. So are our times of disorder and bewilderment, for what are we to do with those who rule us?

Even the best of you lost your reasoning ability, for you let your rulers have no regard for the sanctity of human life. That is why you cannot call the issues by their names nor see your way out of calamity. You let even your own annihilation become acceptable to you.

Mr. President, you sit in the White House surrounded by soulless advisors. An incessant tumult of evil noisemakers assaults your person continually. Your mind can never rest, and no matter what you decide, it is for the wrong. The CIA, the experts, the whizkids, and the military give you no peace. In the Pentagon, too, the blockheads sit in the company of each other. Each one is like his companion. In the inner sanctum where the infamous Red Button lies, the one that may set the world aflame and reduce it to ashes, was not long ago in the hands of an old German Nazi killer (Heutzinger). You, the father of the nation, no longer listen to your own heart. You do not make the decisions any more, nor do you act as you should, as is given to you from on High, when the Glory was conferred upon you and the Burden to carry. You do not hear your children any more. You listen to the counsel of ordinary men who feed you with news clippings and summaries as they deem fit.

Mr. President, why do you permit politics of cruelty? Where do the African nations get the weapons from, to slaughter one another? Why do you deal with Pakistanis and Indians who are at one another's throats continually? Why are Arabs, Indonesians, Cambodians seated side by side with you at the same table? And Syria and Libya are voting members of the Security Council?! You bow to the Chinese ruler out of sheer terror and hold the hand of a mass-murderer. Abnormal reality is called normal now. That is why, in the past, the Fullbrights, the Bundys, the Kissingers, the Hessburghs, the Mitchells were smitten with confusion and ill-advised the president then on Cuba, Viet Nam, on Suez, on Berlin, on Chile and on China, and on all vital matters. Even on most vital matters. And all this continues so today.

You, the people, do not call to task your servants in Congress or Senate; nor do you reproach your president for slackness. Therefore you have advisors who prophesy wrongly and mislead you. From the shadows the grey eminences of the almighty Central Intelligence Agency inform and misinform the government and the public continually. So do your spy systems from across the globe keep Washington, Moscow and Beijing intense. Everything they say, they say in whispers, and everything they see, they see magnified. They gnaw at your hearts and nourish you on fears. And your governments see but through such eyes, and hear but through such ears, and do accordingly. An evil spirit possesses them and they hardly see a way to peace out of conflagration. A bad conscience and mutual fear blind all of you. Wrong counsel and indecision confuse your respective governments. At one time the thinkers, writers, intellectuals had the responsibility, had a moral obligation to care for their people. An ill wind is blowing over and across the earth, all ready to sweep away everything that is dear to you.

Your governments are lulling you into daydreams of security through the balance of terror with resulting prosperity, and you let them. But hear, just listen how awesome the fear that comes from the space bombing platforms, the ABM systems, the FOBS and the MIRVS and all-annihilating weapons. How short of breath you are. Oh, how poisoned you let yourself become by the Von Braunses, the Tellers, the Strausses, the Fullbrights, the Bundys, and the Goldwaters and your other favourite madmen, and still you are today by those who replaced them. The same it is in Russia and China. It is you they are preparing now for violence, for war, and extermination.

And you, the people of Russia and China, you, too, lent your strength to your rulers, supporting even the most cruel tyranny against yourselves. It is with your, the people's, consent that your rulers seethe iniquity among the nations of the Middle East, the Far East, India, Pakistan, Viet Nam, Africa, and South America, and your countries spent themselves on defense against imaginary and provoked aggressors. And your vast and wealthy lands suffer poverty and are unable to nourish their inhabitants and provide for them.

And while both, you Russia and America, waste yourself in mutual fear, from the faraway ends of the earth, a formidable enemy has come up against you, greater and more cruel than yourselves and more ruthless. Like a black cloud gathering in the sky did she gather, China, swift before you had time to turn about. Behold what a harvest of dragons teeth will ye soon reap, ye whitey nations, for the perfidy of your governors. Yes . . . China has woken up and is about ready to swallow both of you in an instant while you drag yourself in morasses of wasteful arguments. Soon at the entrance of each harbour your enemy will stand watch over you with weapons of mass destruction. Every water container of your cities will she

48

spy out to contaminate with bacteria at her whim, at a time uncertain to you. There he is, the huge dragon creeping up upon you from the dense yellow mist, from the swamps of Viet Nam, Laos, Cambodia, Ladakh, Nepal. From Africa, from everywhere, does the immense eery monster crawl towards you. Oh, what a cruel enemy, the Chinese! Their hearts are encrusted against mercy just like your own. They delight in destruction (Lin Piao: "annihilation is acceptable"). They do not reason. They are unaware and know not that they are messengers sent to mend injustices you inflicted upon my children and many other nations.

Yes, it is you, the people of America, Russia and China who delegate the power to those who govern you. You call them "People's Government." Yes, you permit your elected representatives to let them who rule you, oppress you, as if they were Sumerian God-Kings. You hail your rulers, acclaim them, and call them "fathers" lovingly and condone them to draw up policies for destruction. You are silent with consent to the arms race to suicide. Because from these come your most cherished fat, Friday paycheques. You let your rulers bicker about Berlin, about a small dot on the map offshore China, a mountain Tibet, a strip of land in Cambodia, Laos, or Viet Nam . . . unessential for your economies and your security, unessential altogether. Just like quarrelsome couples do, your rulers bark at one another, arguing long after the topic that originated the argument has lost its validity and has been forgotten. They argue out of mere habit nevertheless: like old couples who dislike one another for no tangible reasons.

America and Russia, you have learned naught and have drawn no consequences for the crimes committed but yesterday in the last two world wars. You U.S., Great

Britain and France were the arch culprits for that last war. The Nazis were mere executors of their intent.

The war was very profitable to millions who worked in the armament industries who lived on blood, and seventy million souls paid with their lives for the Second World War, and my seven million Jewish brothers were mere providential lambs you chose to sacrifice. You had not drunk Jewish blood for a long time and everyone was athirst for it. Therefore the Nazis found support in everyone, the U.S., Russia, the neutral nations, the minorities. All eagerly helped to kill Jews. Great Britain and France lost their might and glory for this and or the many other crimes that I would rather not remember but are so hard to forget: The centuries of tormented Africans, and the cries of Asia's children that have risen high, rent the skies and woken up the Lord?! For how else but as a punishment from on High would two powers emerge victorious from such a great war and their conscience croll under their burden?

The empires of Great Britain and France are gone now. The skies over all mankind are thick, clouded and dark with the restless floating souls. Even the flowers in the battlefields still bloom red from the victim's blood, and the shrieks of those killed in Poland and the Ukraine echo in Viet Nam now and the Congo, in Cyprus, and in Indonesia, in the Philippines and in Biafra, in Brazil and Haiti, Bangladesh, and all of South America. In every corner of the globe victims cry, but there is no one left to hear them. The nations of the earth have unlearned how to hear, to have pity and compassion upon one another.

The chief among the nations now are you America and Russia. The crying that comes from all corners of the earth now is your doing, for it is heard. Your counselors are with eyes shut to pity, your rulers hold back their palm from mercy, and you the people of America and Russia, are silent and unmoved.

The great keen killers, those strangers to mercy, the Germans and the Japanese are your allies and friends now. For over fifty years you paid off their hire with blood money, America. That is why you fear the Russians, your allies of yesterday, with a great fear, for you know the iniquity that you secretly bear against them. And you also know that they know this too. A demonic force now attracts you, America, to the killers. Because of sheer immorality the atmosphere between you both is so poisoned. Neither of you has any need of the other, nor are you an obstacle to the other in the pursuit of your favorite way of life. Nevertheless, here you are both victors, former allies, gripped by a deadly fear of one another on the brink of mutual destruction, dragging with yourselves into the abyss most of mankind. Both of you are suspicious of one another. Your listening stations are tuned in on each other day and night, constantly, in dread of incoming missiles.

And you who govern Russia, you make mockery of every human virtue. The callousness with which you trample your own people is unspeakable, and you connive and incite and destroy with fifth columns just about the entire globe. Just look and see the suffering you cause constantly.

*   *   *

The world is now wealthier than ever, yet none of you savour the plenty. It is because of the pillaging that has robbed you of all sense of value and has made you forget how to be friendly while you litigate with one another constantly. See now for yourselves how even in your homes

51

you exhaust yourselves in pointless quarrels with your spouses and neighbours just as your governments do. It is, therefore, that you are unable to transmit your will as men and as people upon your elected rulers, just as in your homes you are grim and angry constantly, and agitated. From one end of the earth to the other everyone is in ire with everyone else without even knowing why.

Just wait a very short while at this pace of events: For a timelessly long minute destruction will flash upon you and the sound of the all-annihilating terror and silence. For the silence that you all kept in the time of need by all who suffered and were tormented. Only silence shall be heard henceforth on the earth. Thus shall the wrath be appeased, and the spirits acquiesced, so the victims return to their abodes from the countless charnel fields. Look around, all of you white mankind now, look around, how your day is closing in on you. Back you are driven to your cradle, herded as if into a sheepfold from your holdings throughout the globe. Is it **your** time now? To meet your appointed last hour? Woe is me . . . all of Africa is stirred up against you. . . . Who has stirred the mighty nations of Asia? Who begot their strength? Is it to rectify evil transgressions? Look and see whiteyman, who, for ages, felt proud, the arbiter of fate. In a mere twenty years, four billion people of colour have risen in arms against you out of an opium-ridden, disorderly mess. See now, if you will, who makes destiny, whose is the might. Do you hear the rumble approaching from the distance? Do the whispers of your secret agents make your bones tremble already? Tel me. Tell me when it comes, and all Time shall reveal itself to you in an instant.

I pray, hear ye not the noises, you who rule Russia, China and America. Forego the tumults that surround you. Hear not what the CIA, FBI, KGB, your Joint Chiefs of Staff, the experts, the whizkids and aparatchiki bark into your ears. Approach one another with a little bit of friendship. Lay politicking aside. Do not condone bloodshed. For the crimes committed against the innocent are crying out in ever larger waves and will fall back upon you certainly. All three of you, U.S.A., Russia, and China, leave this world free, and stop looking upon the small countries of the earth as prey. Let great areas of peace grow between you so that you may grow distant from one another and be less afraid. A step at a time, each one in turn. Withdraw, and cease your subversion, from Africa and Latin America, no matter how secret and well-wrapped. Even NATO you should dissolve altogether for it is no longer essential for your safety. Certainly harbour no evil thoughts as to how you will advance into the others' vacated territories. For that is the cause of your predicament now, that each one of you eyes the other's sphere of influence with envy, greedy to conquer with weapons. Withdraw your defense lines. Do not extend them up into the air and down under water as you are doing now.

The areas of friction will thus diminish. Do not compete lest wrath come wreak its vengeance upon you. Only your children's books of history will bear witness then to what you were, what you did, and what you have left undone. True, by then the Chinese, too, may well be wiped off the face of the earth because of their unequal cruelty or some other reason. Because they, too, will have not heeded that they were but messengers. A mere few lines will tell posterity how . . . "in the first quarter of the 21st century, because of their callousness and insensitivity to human suffering, the Americans and the Russians were defeated by an enemy more cruel than themselves. They were outsmarted and checkmated by the cunning of

China, who wiped them off the surface of the globe together with the rest of white mankind. Having rubbed Europe off the map, they, the Chinese, then occupied Northern America (that was Indian, by the way, before the advent of the white man), and settled 200 million of their people to exploit the riches of the lands once known as Canada and the United States. Thus will have they ruled the world, the commissars from the Imperial Palace of Heavenly Peace. . . ."

> Make peace. Make haste. Make it not too late!
> Make peace. Make haste.

Look my brothers in America, Russia and China! **Look and see what your tyrants do to you!** They blind you fanatical, make you believe that ideologies are paramount to living, and lead you to destruction for "principles." Just like the kings before them, and the ungodly clergy of all creeds, so are your rulers now trying you with the same deceptions: unessential to growing of food and seeing one another with love and compassion and the makings of a good life. They now make democracy and socialism look vital to distract you from the callousness with which they trample you. They know that they are deceiving you, the demagogues keep assuring you of peace while they manufacture the issues that most agitate our times. The pollution and the solution, the crisis, the enemies. And, indeed, the calamity is impending. Your enemy wants your life, all three of them, and there is no way out from perdition lest you quickly act.

For what enemies have you my brothers, men in America, Russia and China, where you all work hard and worry and love and dream of peace, of freedom from uncertainty and want. Your rulers in Washington, Moscow and Beijing are your enemies. These are the men who have quarrels with one another, for all three strive for one and the same end: **Power. Dominion over all of you.**

Rulers are of exceptional ability. They know how to compel, as rulers always did. At their command do nations stand still in obeisance, or hurtle themselves at one another savagely. They are the ones who spark wars and revolutions and drive people, human beings, into the flames of catastrophe, sacrificing millions for their own selfish ends. Those who rule the East and the West hold you bent to their formidable will now. They brought you to the present brink of disaster, as the rulers of the past always did. These of our time, too, will not hesitate to sacrifice you, for they, too, are unfaithful. Let not the lairs poison you, seduce you with words, or drown you in falsehoods. No enemy wants your life, but they who rule you do. They are the cause of all our calamities.

Just look well and see what they do to you.

*   *   *

Most of above I just said may be now obsolete. I very much would like to hope that what I said on the last ten pages is obsolete. The big powers who have the big weapon arsenals all know that these are unusable. Ever since Gorbachev stepped forward and declared it to all. Thus the nations embarked another fight. The struggle has become with one another's economies. Instead of being constructive and supportive of one another, the three big powers compete with each other. Each want to outproduce the others to the point of economic bankruptcy to themselves and their competitors.

To what purpose is that? A confusion has stricken all major powers who could and should be partners in the global economies are competing deadly with one another since the various GATT and WTO and other insane arrangements were introduced. Their people are exhausted breathless heading for unemployment and poverty. Just to illustrate a clear example: 100,000 American textile workers are laid off and their work is now done by Chinese workers. To maintain the balance of payments, a few hundred American hi-tech workers produce in exchange to the now imported Chinese textiles. The balance of payments tally all right. The 100,000 American workers however remained unemployed. That is the real balance and not the dollar balance.

I am unable to stop my lament and my mournful cry. For you, made in the image of the Lord, did not care. You always waited to blame "the maker of destiny" for all that happens to you. An entity you don't believe exists at all, and you still call **God Almighty**, when it is convenient to you.

Morality dissolved. People's government, totalitarian or democratic, is a farce. They are all oligarchies. Business is booming but life is worthless. Four-fifths of the global population is coloured and their cumulative and well justified wrath will explode upon you soon, who bloats now with power and pride. It's the year 2001:

Do not discard at all the accidental destruction of the entire globe. For an anarchy rules the world. Anarchy of literally insane little despots who still believe in power through mass destructive weapons in their hands feasible. Small despots with limited intelligence possess weapons and are with no consideration of the consequences: Chechens, Ayatollahs, Saddams, Bin Ladins, Qadaffis and their ilk are out of control. Not the U.S. nor Russia nor Europe can reason with these people whom they bred with intent and purpose quite differently than has turned out to be. It is backfiring now on all of mankind. Your perverted rulers were hatching murderers for the remnant of my people. These have turned upon you all and you stand now benumbed and helpless. Reason is not valid any longer. The end of all of you is very close at hand. Tell me now what you want to do and how will you change this and collect all the deadly weapons from the many mad men who hold them. How much weight can man carry on his conscience? How much weight can your conscience carry?

Do you know why atrocities were committed from their very onset to date? **Because you did not care**. Then. Nor today do you care. You are "busy."

No one demanded even a line of contrite sorrow from the Americans for the atrocities they committed on the native Indians 150 years ago, or for the Vietnam massacres of the 1970s. No one demanded an apology and restitution for the killing of the 10 million Congolese children from the Belgians. No one apologized or expressed sorrow for the murder of the Armenians, the doings of the Japanese in Manchuria. No one asked them to show repentance for what they did to live victims, experimenting on them, in the Second World War. No one sincerely or meaningfully regretted the extermination of my brothers, and hundreds of millions of other by now:

No one reprimanded the rulers of China for what they did to people—their own people! This is called "politics" in our time.

It's the year 2003. The Chinese sit side by side in the United Nations of cannibals. Because of their size and multitude, they are accorded supreme honours. But so does Idi Amin, who is greeted upon arrival to the U.S. with a 21-gun salute and a standing ovation in the great hall of the UN. Because he publicly extols Hitler and calls my nation racists. He is dined in the White House by the

President of the U.S., while, the day before, he ate parts of his wife! (just as I said it!!—he also keeps in his freezer small children to be eaten, stuffed with rice!!) He is friendly with everyone, the Arab sheiks, and princes. As a matter of fact, Idi Amin is ruler no longer. He is retired now, and lives in a 70-room mansion with his many wives and children in Saudi Arabia as a guest for life of his Royal Highness King Saud.

The details of the friendship of Giscard D'Estang, President of France, with Emperor Bokassa are well known. The former "emperor," his family, and entourage were given imperial refuge in a castle on the French Riviera with bodyguards by the President of France. So was Papa Doc Duvalier's gorilla son.

He just passed away, one more favourite son of all the nations who came to visit the UN frequently. He strode to the podium with two guns dangling from his sides and waved an olive branch in a cobra headdress with a sneer, and all the UN delegates jumped to their feet for a standing ovation: "Heil! Sieg heil! Ecce homo!" There is their man! He will kill all the Jews and push them into the sea. All roared and cheered "A-ra-fat-A-ra-fat-A-ra-fat!" He was no head of state. He was no delegate of any member nation, but he was all your Man. He would kill the Jews. And, indeed, he promised all you wanted to hear, and you wanted to hear all he promised. He would drown all the accursed yids into the sea. There will be no usurper Polish-Jewish riff-raff arrivals to occupy Jerusalem, defile the Holy Sepulture and oppress the Holy land of the Bedouin. He would make good the dreams of the British, the French, of Adolf Hitler, the Christians, and all the nations of Allah who, of course, will help as well! "Seig Heil!"

Then, finally, you will be able to get at one another's throats freely and have a feast of a holocaust! And there will be no more Jews to point the fingers at your conscience! Finally you can eat one another in broad daylight and have the Final Solution for which you are so desirous.

*   *   *

What that Schickelgruber did in 12 years to man's mind is **mind boggling**. The tyrants multiplied in number and size until they assumed giant proportions, A.H., Lenin, Stain, Mao, Bokassa, Amin, Duvallier, Saddam, Kaddafi, Kim all dwarf the Neros and Calligulas of two thousand years ago.

So the Lord God of the heavens was swallowed up by the earthly rulers whom you gave all your collective strength and worship now, fear, bow down and adulate to.

Each of the **great tyrants** today want to be the **sole God**. Therefore, they need wars. To eliminate the opponents of their sole lordship. And you helped them all the way and still do. Because these wars where you are the killers make you, too, feel omnipotent and godlike, just like your ruler you emulate and to whom you lent your strength. All of you. To make him powerful, almighty over you. That's what makes you obey and be like him.

Destiny, which is mostly the work of the people as they arrange it for themselves, has metaphysical laws, that balance. Thus, with the wonderful WWII, science bloomed and blossomed, fantastic mass-destruction weapons were invented, supersonic bombers, AVACS, missiles, atomic, biological and chemical weapons. Yes, you managed even to reach the moon, mostly in a quest to learn about FOBs, MIRVs and space-bombing platforms. Eventually all this has come back to us.

The hundred million victims killed in the first half of the 20th century, and the five hundred million killed in

59

the second half, have no rest. Their piercing cries surround the Van Allen belt. No, they do not let you rest. They don't let you sleep at night. Insanity rules your mind with all its consequences.

Today, 55 years later, A.H. lives in the hearts and minds of millions. Mengele and other angels of death roam the earth freely. You think I exaggerate? **Just think!**

In Brazil, young gangs roam the favelas and kill captured, healthy teenagers and dismember them professionally, trained in every detail to put their organs, eyes, hearts, lungs, kidneys, liver, into proper vessels into sterile jars with perfect liquid to be transported to medical centers for resale worldwide to sick recipients for big money. A new industry in the 20th century, thanks to the various Mengeles' initial research. Is your hair not standing up?

I am no prophet, nor a prophet's son. I am an ordinary villager who tended sheep and worked at menial jobs. I am desperate and refuse to carry the message of that Lord who has showed no compassion to man's pain and ignorance for the last 250 years.

I do not want to go Niniveh! No way! Send your whale and let her swallow me! Let her not spit me out on any shore! From the depths of that whale I will cry then as I do now, unless You make man merciful again and compassionate to one another. I do not want to be Your messenger unless You show your mercy and put compassion and love into the heart of all mankind. Unless you change the human heart. My life is a curse onto me.

II

Israel—
My Precious,
Unfortunate
Israel

2

Israel—My Precious, Unfortunate Israel

Fraternal dissidy comes with our genes.
Will it be enough if I begin with our patriarchs?
Three times the Lord promises Abraham
"All this land will be yours forever."[*]
Abraham circumcises himself as a token of this
    covenant.
Then Sarah dies one page later and he buys her tomb
and a cave from Uri, the Hittite, for four hundred
    shekels.
Abraham, his sons Ishmael and Isaac
Isaac and his sons, Jacob and Esau,
Jacob and his twelve sons and daughter,
The sons of the three founding patriarchs
Abraham, Isaac and Jacob tore at one another
    incessantly.
Reuben, Judah, The Dinah affair.
Joseph was sold by his own brothers into slavery
Joseph and the consequences of the descent to Egypt
Cost 400 years of building pyramids.

[*]Genesis Chapter 15, Verse 17; Genesis Chapter 22, Verse 17; Deuteronomy Chapter 1

This wasn't very loving of the Lord.
Moses had to use very drastic measures
to get the Jews out of Egypt.
For they refused to be liberated just to subject
        themselves
to some suspect new restrictions.
Finally they left for an uncertain future and
forty years of incessant arguments.
They knew that the Promised Land has a high price,
so they took upon themselves the Ten Commandments,
and the rest of the 613 obligations grudgingly.
From forty years of sheer arguments and aggravation
Moses died, though he very much wanted aliah.
Yes, I skipped one detail! Moses committed a
        transgression:
He hit the stone instead of talking to it.
So all the 1001 good things he did for the Lord did not
        count.
He would not let him enter the so-much-coveted Land of
        Israel.
The Jews entered Canaan where they continued the
        tradition
of freedom of opinion and continued bickering.
(Every two Jews had three opinions).
Joshua married the Madam of the Jericho casino
Although intermarriage was a rock-bottom no-no.
("Exterminate all the Indians or else you will never
        inherit.")
Canaan was not conquered exactly as instructed.

                    *   *   *

    After Joshua there were more or less two hundred
years of benevolent anarchy during the time of the

judges, at which time "everybody did whatever they pleased." (After all, if Joshua who spoke with God was permitted, why not us?) The six tribes that did not conquer and settle remained nomads among indigenous nomads. They did as they pleased.

This imperfect but quite idyllic arrangement stopped when the people suddenly wanted to have a king, like the other nations. Samuel warned them that an earthly king is much more costly to upkeep than the king in heaven. No: They wanted an earthly king. So they got themselves Saul, a certified schizo, just because he was the tallest among them. He was followed by David. I will not enter into the details of David's carryings on. There is hardly an evil that he did not commit between writing the psalms, including making out with a Hittite soldier's wife, the heir to the throne, Solomon. I fail to understand how he got away with all this. He managed even to become our seventh patriarch.

Solomon outdid his father by quite a bit. He built the House of the Lord and a palace for himself, and temples and palaces for his numerous wives and their gods. For this he squeezed the blood out of his people with compulsory labour and taxes. The temple was standing but hardly anyone was attending. Thus Solomon reigned wisely and lived well and elegantly for forty years, until he died.

Several pretenders to his throne arose and the nation split in two. Ten tribes with a more liberal religious legislation, and Judah with Benjamin and the temple. The country fell further apart when the pretenders attacked each other in a fratricidal war. In one such engagement alone, 120,000 men of Israel fell. So the losers, the ten tribes, called in the Assyrians for help against their own brothers, and when the Assyrians came and saw what state the Israelis were in, they simply took the entire ten tribes on a one-way trip to Kolyma (read Assyria), never to return or to be heard of again. (Judea did not come to the rescue.) The leftover Jews continued tearing at one another for another hundred years or so. They also committed some things "that were evil in the eyes of the Lord," so He sent Josif Visarionovitch Nebuchadnezar, who destroyed the Lord's house and all the other houses of Jerusalem complete, and took all the Jews to behind the Polar Circle (read Babylon).

While marching several hundred miles into captivity with chains on their necks, the argumentative "pilpul" did not leave the Jews and they continued to compose the Babylonian Talmud on the road.

Cyrus, with a group of Medean shepherds, came and undid the Empire of Babylon. Cyrus, and later Darius, were kind to the leftover Jews and let them return from Siberia (read Babylon) and rebuild the temple in Jerusalem. The temple they rebuilt was only half the size of the one before, but there was no more Shechina,—the spirit of the Lord of Israel resided there no longer.

The Persians and the Jews got along pretty well, until a new conqueror arrived, Alexander the Great, and took over the Persian Empire. The Greeks did not like the Jews because of philosophical differences and jealousy, and they were going to undo the Temple again. So, a group of Jews called Hashmonaim organized themselves and waged a partisan war against the Greeks until they annoyed them enough to leave. The Greeks went home. Nevertheless, the next few hundred years were constant belligerence and turmoil for Israel and all the neighboring small countries.

The Jews again did something they shouldn't have, and "were evil in the eyes of the Lord" (perhaps they drove cars on Shabat, wore miniskirts or bikinis on the beach—I'm not sure what straw broke the camel's back).

The Lord got mad, and sent the Romans upon us. And from there on it all went downhill. (That JC with his new bible from where he erased half of the prohibitions did not help things either.) To make the story short, the Romans or the Lord destroyed his own house and everyone else's house again and sent the Jews wandering for nearly two thousand years all around the globe. He Himself stood by all this unmoved, as if it were not His business at all. Of course, the 613 Commandments are good but they are very hard to keep. So there may have been some fornicating with the natives, or trefe meat, or marijuana—big deal. For that you undo an entire nation?! I don't think very well of this either. You know the rest of the history of the last two thousand years. It was a history of regular holocausts of those elected children of the Lord. I will skip the details of all those centuries of our most inglorious history of which our Lord should not be proud either, for He contributed to our destruction most. Why did He give us Isaiah and Malachi; what good did they do to their generation? Write beautiful speeches? Would they have all received Nobel Prizes? Why did He not give us Malcolm X, Farrakhan, J. Jackson?

*   *   *

He did give us an encyclopedic list of sages and scholars bright as stars during the past 2000 years, but they did not alleviate the nation's physical persecutions one iota.

From 1900–2000 we 12 million little nation of Jews collected more Nobel Prizes than the several billion people of the entire world, contributing with our learning and knowledge to all people's advance and welfare; still, we did not stave off the united drive of inhumanity to annihilate us in that very time.

(I wish to tread on nobody's toes, as I was brought up in a small Karpathian village in an Orthodox Jewish home, and consider myself an Orthodox Jew to the present day. I will just not be terrorized by cripple-minded little dictators of what orthodoxy is.)

*   *   *

We are at about 1880 now and the pogroms are spreading in Russia, killing Jews wholesale, so a number of Jews who loved their homeland passionately founded the Hibat Zion Organization and decided to go back **Home**, to Israel. About 25,000 made Alijah[*] 1882–85.

At the same time in Austria an honourable man, Theodor Herzl, an emancipated Jewish newspaperman himself, saw that in spite of the enlightened gentile promises, the Jews will not survive. The gentiles no matter what their promises and assurances did not like the Jews. He wrote a small booklet Der Judenstaat in 1896, a sort of manifesto about the problems of the Jews and their solutions. He had very few faithful friends, Max Nordau, Leo Pinsker, who worked with him wholeheartedly. Their aim was similar to that of Hibat Zion: let's go back **Home** to **Our Land**.

Herzl set up speaking tours across Europe, established a weekly Jewish newspaper, *Die Welt*, and with numerous articles won enough followers for his idea, that he

*Ascent

called for the first Zionist congress to convene in Basel in 1897. With acclamation of all the delegates he was proclaimed president of the newly founded Zionist organization. The Basel program of the conference also called for repossessing the land of our forefathers, our Land. Herzl did not have much opposition except Achad Haam and a small group of associates. The arguments were mostly trivial, due to envy and petty jealousy. In 1904, Herzl died of heartache.

In 1905 the Russian revolution precipitated a large wave of pogroms again and 40,000 Jews came to kiss the soil and love the land of their forefathers.

In 1911 Javnieli brought several thousand returnees from Jemen and Buchara. By 1914 there were 85,000 Jews in Israel. In 1909 Tel Aviv was founded with 2,000 Jews, Haifa had 3,000 Jews followed by Herzlia, Binjamina, and the Land grew.

In 1906 a young demagogue in the making, David Green by name, came to the land of Israel and like all demagogues of the time, was a burning socialist who admired Lenin. He formed the Achdut Haavoda, that is the Labourers Union which became the socialist Histadrut in short time. Like every demagogue, Lenin, Stalin and others had their own ideas that did not tally at all with what they were lying about to the people. David Green was no different. (For him a state is founded and organized for its own sake and the benefit of the Oligarchs, and organizers: quote Leibowitz—The people are mere subjects.)

In 1917, the Ottoman Empire was defeated during the First World War and the territory that they called Palestine was mandated by the league of nations to administer to the British.

The Jews negotiated with the British about that little piece of territory that was really ours for millennia.

The British pretended to be polite and Lord Balfour even said that the Jews should be given a claim to this little piece of stone and desert.

The president of the U.S., W. Wilson, a great Jew sympathizer, thought quite differently: "Just because the Jews were there 2000 years from Abraham to the destruction of the temple, it is absurd to give them still now the right of ownership." Now, remember, we are dealing with the same British who didn't give a hoot when two million innocent Armenians who were massacred as they were looking on. These people should care about the Jews?! But we were licking their boots and negotiating anyway. The negotiations went back and forth several years on the Paris Conference in 1919, the San Remo conference in 1920. Our future state president, Weitzman, explicitly replied NO, If the Jews want an autonomous Jewish government in Palestine: "We want a little Monaco with a university."

The leadership of the Zionist movement was now in the hands of inconsiderate, selfish socialists who had little in common with the spirit of our people or with our heritage or with our Lord, all concepts that had kept us alive for millennia. The Ben Gurionchiks (Mister Green changed his name to "Son of a Lion cub"), Weitzman, Usishkin, Rupin, Achad Haam, Katznelson, Borochow, and their similar self proclaimed demagogues imposed themselves on the assembly of simpletons inexperienced in perversions of politics, the poor Jewish proletariat.

*   *   *

The Histadrut was organized so as to guarantee self-perpetuating elitism.

70

1. Histadrut members elect delegates to the convention which is not elected directly by the voters.
2. The convention elects a Council that elects the Executive Committee.

The Histadrut elected delegates owe nothing to the voters.

The Council's "supervision" of the Executive Committee is a farce to this day.

*   *   *

The new self-proclaimed demagogues put up a Keren Kajemet and Keren Hajesod for the purpose of organizing a new Jewish state.

They set up an "organization" of professional schnorrers who got a percentage of the collected monies to finance the new enterprise. They milked money mainly from the poor, but the rich as well. Money poured in, and the organization men became bureaucrats, i.e., managers. They set up elegant offices, dressed well, fressed well and slowly started setting up an estate.

The whole organization of little Polish mediocrities started to "buy a country." Their original own country. In the history of all mankind, such an absurdity never happened.

That petty smallpox-faced beggar from Plonsk, our future president, Mr. Weitzman, put on a burnus and a kaffieh and had himself photographed with a real sheik (what an honor; did the sheik put on a talit?!) for the purpose of buying back our own country. That was our future leaders' brightest idea, to buy our land from nomad Bedouin shepherds who happened to graze there (illegally).

Our Fathers' land from the nomad bedouin whom the Turks brought in less than 100 years ago, and later by the British to counterweigh the Jewish immigration. They were going to buy back from these foreign nomads our own Land, for which we are the only nation on earth to possess a written deed 4,000 years old. Real estate, desert, sand and stone from Bedouins who were never conscious of claiming it as their own. It was worthless to them because they knew it was never theirs. But as soon as they smelled money from these Jews wanting to buy their own land, the illiterate nomads had a real prank with the demented Yids, and promptly proclaimed themselves owners (especially with British help) and were ready to "sell."

Just as in Soviet Russia, where the politicians control and manage the economy, the Zionist demagogues did the same thing. Labour Zionism of the Jewish proletariat and its economic and political management were in the hands of ruthless oligarchs. Politicians controlled the economy without regard to efficiency or profitability. They also took over with an iron fist: education, public broadcast, news publication, public transportation, banking, agriculture, housing, and the most important industries that they organized as cartels whose prices they dictated. After 1948 all major economic enterprises that were in the hands of the British passed to the Histadrut; that was the de facto government.

All railway, air, and sea transportation, EL AL, ZIM, energy production, oil, cement, agricultural products, citrus marketing and the important of most vital commodities became all government monopolies. Defense, electronics, aircraft, and heavy armour industries were likewise government monopolies headed by favourite managers.

Housing was most unequally administered by the government and only prominent Histadrut members got elite accommodations for next to nothing. The proletariat lived as they did in other socialist countries in most depressing tenements.

The bureaucracy is so oppressive that to open a small business in Tel-Aviv, one needs eleven permits and **"connnections."**

Everyone's wages are determined by politicians, irrespective of worker's productivity or an employer's profitability. The bureaucratic elite gets on top of their "wages," "benefits," and "amenities," "expenses"—automobile, food, loans, mortgages, residences—the repayment of which are depending on connections and are often waived.

The dominant political party of the Histadrut became the de facto government of Palestine's (Israel's) Jewish proletariat and citizens.

BG: The expertise of Histadrut functionaries is not in business administration but in devotion to Zionism. The question is not whether our comrades are honest and experienced, but whether they are good Zionists.

The hegemony of Labour is a bluff up to the present day. It's a Hegemony of self-appointed labour oligarchy. They did not administer a state, they managed their own estate, the oligarchy's estate.

The word Jishuv was not accidental. It meant settlement (temporary), not a definite state. What did they know about running a state? Nothing! They set up an agenda of what they would do with the land of sand and stone and marshes. They wrote propaganda pamphlets to attract immigrants and set up an Israel.

I must stop at once!—The word Israel never came up

in their mind until 20–25 years later. They started out to set up an **estate** as any large South American or Texan or Australian estates were, except this little estate was really small.

They harnessed the newcomers with the idea that they must prove themselves, that they were good labourers of the land and not mere merchants and usurers as the gentiles saw them, and as these new ruling oligarchy also made them feel that they were. They pressed them to become one hundred percent socialists, and brothers to all the other socialist nations who had no intention to socialize with Jews, but keep them out from their brotherhood. These new misleaders never had a hoe in their hands, never laid a brick to a house, and kept our people down instead of uplifting them lovingly and reassuring them of how wonderful they were. The new Histadrut oligarchy trod with iron boots the poor newly arrived Jews into the hardest and most merciless reclamation of the land that had been fallow for two thousand years. Just like the Soviet commissars organized the entire rural and urban Jishuv mostly for their own sakes.

The little Communist dictator in disguise, Ben Gurion, admired Lenin so much that he went to meet him to the new Soviet Union although by then, Lenin was a noted wholesale killer of millions in the name of socialist justice.

To wake you up for real, I must re-write the fictitious history written by the founders of this unlucky little land, conceived with initial good intent by Herzl but the leadership of which was highjacked quickly after his death, by selfish egotist types of Marx and Lenin, who knew exactly what they wanted.

They wanted everything. And all that for themselves. The "people," the state, were a fraudulent prop set up to

74

get all they had premeditated in advance: No, there was to be no sharing. The underlings for whom the new little dictators planned a few good jobs for later, ministerial, ambassadorial, etc., jobs were to be mere servants for his sole self-centered purpose: what the little dictator in chief wanted them to be, serfs.

BG knew his own boundless egotism. He didn't have the territory or the numbers of people to become a God like the other big dictators of the time, so he became the best he could, a selfish little egotist disguised in the simplicity of clothes (as did the Emperor Mao with his gray tunic later), with everyone bent down crawling before him scraping the ground. All his cronies were moulded for his purpose in his own image. There wasn't one single man with an independent mind to stand up to him in that unlucky little country in the making.

In 1948, a special assembly was elected to write the country's constitution and prepare elections for the Knesset. Instead of doing so, the assembly appointed itself as the first Knesset. Because Israel had no constitution, the Knesset's power was absolute. It can enact anything a majority of its members fancy, unhindered by checks and balances. It could pass retroactive laws and has done so more than once in order to nullify High Court rulings. Furthermore, there is no separation between the legislative and executive branches of government. All these vast powers of state are concentrated in the hands of the Knesset and the cabinet, which are mostly Knesset members.

One of the first acts of the Knesset was to enact Law on Privileges, Obligations and Immunity of Knesset Members. An MK shall not be responsible, criminally or civilly, for anything he does in his job or outside of it. MKs have rarely, yes, been accused of criminal acts. E.g., MK

Yitzhak Rafael, was indicted for bribery, and so were MKs Rechtman, Abuhatzeira, Flatto-Sharon, and others. The government's legal advisor did lodge a motion for the revocation of immunity of these criminals, but he was rejected and even threatened unless he revoked the indictment.

The Cabinet has 25 ministers and six deputy ministers, who devote much of their time to party politics.

Just as Lenin and Stalin did, they organized a "Nomenclatura" based on distribution of sinecures to their friends, buying loyalties, and so they succeeded to organize a strong cadre of usurpers extending from the very top to the last little postman and village policeman who gave them the support they needed. And just to show that they were not real dictators they permitted various groups to have voiceless opinions so that it could all be called democracy—a laugh. Only the Herut, with Jabotinski and Begin, could claim a confused program and inept leadership (Jabotinski applied to Petljura, a noted Jew killer to train for him the right-wing gendarmerie, and Begin applied to the Nazis that his party members could wear brown shirts and black-belted uniforms, as if such uniform made them any different).

The right-wing demagogues were not much different from the left-wing ones. They did not care for the people or for Israel, only for the money pot and the palatial residences that emanate power.

This little **estate** (please note, not "state") grew from all this new organized schnorred money. The pathetic little thieves of the left, the right, and the religious grew rapacious and brutal. Out of nothing, in a short time thirty-seven different "parties" formed, none of them with a single line of genuine ideology or thought. Not a single loving heartbeat for the Jewish people or our precious new Homeland, Israel. Israel was not in their minds at all when they started out. They knew nothing of governing a country. They were busy arguing and tearing at one another for a bigger portion of the looted dough for their own sake mainly. They schnorred around the globe. They all wanted to be leaders. The organization grew now worldwide and called itself the Zionist Organizations of Israel, of America, and of the World.

Two-thirds of Israel's wage-earners were employed directly or indirectly by the government or the Histadrut, with about the lowest wages in the Western World and the average earnings per month is about $350. That hardly covers the minimum cost of living. The government budget is equal to the GNP nearly 100 percent, just like in the Soviet block countries, in contrast to Western democracies, where the budget is one third or maximum one half of the GNP.

In Russia, China or Cuba, socialism was enforced through violence against the people. **In Israel socialist rule was established years before the state even existed.**

One Israeli in nine has left the country. Israel has the highest per capita debt in the Western world and the lowest labour productivity. Taxes are the highest; emigration is the highest. Price and wage controls are the highest.

Yes Israel has achieved some great things. It has the world's largest number of scientific publications relative to population; the highest number of scientists per person with advanced technological education; agrotechnical capabilities and developments in the fields of instrumentation and irrigation which experts from all over the world visit Israel to study. It has the world's record per capita new book titles published. It has an army of superb fighters and owns the most advanced weapons development and production systems.

Yet all these achievements are dwarfed by Israel's potential: Because of the politization of the bureaucratic system, the waste of public resources, citizens' dependence on government, and its inability to control government activity.

*   *   *

But let me describe now shortly how our Zionist leaders led us to Birkenau, Belzec, Majdanek, Sobibor, Treblinka. You may want to get livid, furious with me for this. Go right ahead, I will not be offended.

I will not retract from this statement a single word.

*   *   *

In 1925, the University of Jerusalem was established. The Histadrut oligarchy permitted a powerful elite of university professors, mostly of German and American origin, to come in, who, in turn, wanted to force upon the meager Jishuv an Arab-Jewish peace association, and wanted, at all cost, to negotiate democratically with our assassins about our Land.

They were fighting tooth and nail against the establishment of a Jewish state in our **Homeland**. "Zionism is a recent invention of a self-possessed racist minority. It's illegal, immoral and anti-democratic to take away this land of our fathers from these poor recent inhabitants, and establish the state of Israel": Martin Buber, Juda Magnes, Hugo Bergman, Albert Einstein, Werner Senator, the Warburg banking family, the Sears Roebucks,

Gershon Sholem, Henrietta Szold, the *New York Times* owner Ochs and many other big names from the American and British Zionist executive, American Rabbis' Conference, the German Rabbis' Association, all declared Zionism intolerable. The British appointed Herbert Samuel, a Jew, governor of Palestine, who installed Amin Husseini as the Grand mufti of Jerusalem (despite the fact that he had already a 14–year sentence on him for crimes committed before.) Husseini promptly unleashed massacres of Jews in Hebron, Zfat, Jerusalem and other places, but the Jews did not defend themselves from these pogroms "because that is not Jewish."

These Jekkes of the Jerusalem University, who were atheists, went demented entirely: "The Jewish soul" (they dared speak about the soul these soulless creatures), which was 2,000 years spiritual will descend into materialism the moment they acquired their Land from the Arabs and Bedouin. The minimum compromise they propagated was to live in a bi-national state where we would be a one-tenth minority versus the Arabs, who were promoted to be legitimate owners ever since Mohammed took off on his horse, Burak, in the seventh century from our Temple Mount, and therefore has a claim of precedence of ownership, our demented intelligentsia declared. The fact that we lived in this land, 3,300 years before Mohammed was born, and that the Arabs did not exist at all, the Jekkes did not want to hear about. Especially since our socialist traitors, BG, and the Histadrut "did not look," ever since the Hebrew University of Jerusalem was established. The professors, mostly of German-Jewish descent, kept on hammering their views into their students. These students pervaded with time every leading administrative position of the evolving Jewish state. The should-be fathers of our nation, didn't hear, didn't see and didn't look, when our arch-enemies from within were destroying us.

*   *   *

Between 1929–39, both the U.S. and Europe were in a severe economic crisis. In spite of all prohibitions written post WWI, the U.S. and GB started to rearm Hitler for war. They agreed with him secretly to make a war again. "A pretend war" that would get all industry rolling on both sides of the ocean and get the economy going. After the war, which will cause damage to Germany of course, the U.S. and GB promised to rebuild the German Reich anew, to last a thousand years, just the way Hitler dreamt about. (The Marshall Plan for German reconstruction was prepared in advance.)

For Roosevelt and Churchill, this was a terrific rescue operation, from the depression of the U.S. and GB of the thirties.

The Allies knew about Hitler's Jew-extermination plan, (did they not plan it together?) And his plan to kill all the Commies and to expand his territory across Poland and the USSR right up to the Urals.

Ben Gurion also knew all the details about the Jew extermination plans. All the bearded, sidelocked, kaftaned, hunchbacked Jews so desperately poor, and their wives and children, would be all killed. Thus the problem of accommodation of millions of our fellow Jews in Israel would be solved. BG and his gang promised to the Allies they would **"not look"** when the war got going. And they didn't. "The Holocaust should be treated as a natural disaster. It is not the Jewish agency's business to save the Jews of Europe but to build the land of Israel."

The Histadrut was already preparing the future.

They were distributing sinecures and management of all big government socialized wealth to about 20 top favorite members of the nomenclatura, and all this wealth was privatized and handed over to the sons of the founders for a pittance. (Israel is now, in the year 2000, owned by a powerful oligarchy of about 20 families.)

The world Jewish Organization, the Zionist organization of all the political parties of Israel, managed practically not to save a single Jew during the entire war. Because they were too busy rebuilding the Jishuv from socialist to private.

The Zionist executives knew their accounting: if seven million Jews will be killed in the next war, the seven hundred thousand Jishuvniks will inherit the wealth of ten exterminated families each and life will be a bowl of cherries with no more headaches about how to accommodate all these poor brothers in this little land. (Quote Eshkol, Jitzchak Gruenbaum, Weizman, "We cannot possibly accommodate all these crazy Jews in this little Land." Henrietta Szold "Send them back!"—They did go back to Bremen—Auschwitz) "All the Jewish problems will be solved in this final solution: And this little Israel will be all ours. All ours! All ours!!—We will be rich!"

Ben Gurion and the Histadrut, the virtual governors of the country, promised and pledged to the U.S. and GB **"not to look,"** and, indeed, they didn't.

It's 1926 now, and the Mein Krach, (Mein Kampf) was already waved passionately from thousands of fists with all the details of Hitler's program for the Jews. He was just about to win his elections in Germany, which he did in 1933. The Zionist executive (Ben Gurion) sent him a congratulatory telegram on his victory. No, I am not drunk and not making this up. As a matter of fact, shortly afterwards Hindenburg who was Hitler's patron, died and the Zionist executive sent Hitler a condolence telegram.

Arthur Rupin corresponded amicably "with Baron Mildenstein (Eichmann's predecessor), and the Sturmer struck a commemorative medal on Mildenstein's visit to Israel with a swastika on one side and the star of David on the other side.

Arlazarov went to Berlin to visit with Magda Goebbels for some irrational negotiations to mollify Hitler. Dachau, Buchewald, Mauthausen concentration camps were already established. The Jews were expelled from many occupations, and were thrown out of their houses. The Kristallnacht had already been arranged by the SA thugs. The British emigration quota to Israel was limited to 25,000 Jews yearly for fourteen million doomed European Jews.

The global Jewish intelligentsia, the artists, scientists, thinkers, Nobel Prize winners, were also incredibly busy with the ongoing U.S. war effort. They too had no time to save a single Jew to speak of "even one was too many."

You won't believe what terrific business this busy-ness was. As soon as the war was finished, in 1946 and onward, the 700,000 Jews in the Jishuvs in Israel discovered indeed, that each one had at least 10 relatives murdered in Poland, Germany, and all over Europe, and that they were now the heirs to all that wealth and even to the gold melted from their tooth fillings and wedding rings. These were suddenly all **theirs! All this wealth was theirs!**

For public consumption, of course, they never forget to cry and shout aloud that the gentiles, who, as everyone always knew, even the gentiles themselves, hated the Jews, and "they" killed their brothers. (Suddenly the victims became their brothers.) Indeed, there was a long list of perpetrators to be blamed for the killings. No, no! I am not absolving them from our holocaust, not the Germans who turned on the gas in the gas chambers, nor the Ukrainians and Lithuanians, etc., killers who were shooting my brothers into the ditches, the victims had to dig for themselves. **The main culprits for all the above however were our world Jewish, Israeli, Zionist misleaders!**

No! I will not withdraw a single syllable from this statement of why the seven million holy Jews were killed: I repeat, **because their own Jewish brothers pushed them into the gas chambers and execution pits!**

The Wiedergutmachung money, which literally translates "**money that makes all good again,**" rectified all, and everything that happened and that initially in 1945–46–47, looked as if the Germans penitently were going to "make good with." What a laugh!

*   *   *

I am quoting from Tom Segev's book *The Seventh Million,* page 244 and page 251:

Adenauer gave instructions that the Wiedergutmachung Treaty include a provision ensuring that only a single Israeli company would receive merchandise from Germany to prevent "Jewish profiteers" from flooding the German market. "I know no other nation with so many thieves, con men, and profiteers lacking all conscience as this tiny nation called Israel," the German minister wrote.

The Germans did not pay much. Every citizen of Germany paid out about 40 marks a year ($10) for fifteen years. That was true as of 1967. The Germans later figured that, by the year 2030, they would have paid out 120 billion marks (between $30 and $60 billion, in keeping with changes in exchange rate). This was the sum that approximately 60 million Germans would pay out over 75 years, the average per person coming to **26 marks a year—about half a mark (25 cents) a week.** A large part of that money was intended as payment for property confiscated by the Germans that remained in their hands. There is no reason to divide the total sum the Germans paid by the number of Jews they murdered, but neither does such a formula give an impressive result in actuarial terms: 120 billion marks for six million victims come to 20,000 marks per person, between $5,000 and $10,000 over the 75 years.

Furthermore, the Germans never had to pay a single cent of Wiedergutmachung out of their pockets, thanks to the genius of the foremost American business schools. The money, mountains of it, was Jewish: City blocks, land holdings and other properties, factories, bank accounts, art collections, worth billions of dollars that belonged to us were kept by the thieves. Not a penny had to be returned, not even the tons of gold fillings from the victims' teeth and wedding rings melted down and kept in *"neutral"* Switzerland with huge bank accounts which took 50 years for the righteous Swiss people to confess were in their possession. (Only by the mistaken blurb of a middle-rank banking clerk who supervised the shredding up of the pre-war Jewish deposit papers did the truth come to light.) No, nothing had to be given back to the Jews. Israel got goods made in Germany, which enriched the **German workers** by billions all over again, and every German household benefited from this German loot a second time, working day and night in their factories or the originally Jewish factories, for extraordinary wages.

This time my Jewish Zionist brothers, who had declared themselves heirs to these fortunes left all the loot to the good Germans who sent for all these billions, for the houses and lands and factories, gold, cash deposits, etc., to Israel goods made by Volkswagen and Krupp, Messerschmidt, IG Farben, Siemens and other products and made the Germans rich all over again. This time for real. The Warburgs bought after the war the division of IG Farben that produced the cyanide that gassed the Jews. (What's wrong with that? You may ask. Why it's a good business. It gases insects and has many other good applications!)

*   *   *

No country became as wealthy after the "lost war" as the Fuhrer's Reich, which the victorious Allies promised to him in advance would be rebuilt to last a thousand years. First the autobahn was rebuilt for the Fuhrer's Volkswagen. Then came the Fressvelle, Reisevelle, Kurvelle, Whorevelle, which, thanks to the KdF org. left by Hitler spread globally. It's Whorevelle now worldwide.

Now that things had gone on so well and had been settled amicably between the Israeli Schweinhunds and their German counterparts, no one needed to worry about Nazi executioners anymore. Prosecution and justice for the killers, "who only did their duty on the fuhrer's order" anyway (and the fuhrer, luckily, was no more to deny this).

The Mengeles, Mullers, Wirths, and Globoczniks multiplied and spread worldwide, thanks to their American and British sponsors (the Catholic Church helped, too, in the critical post war years.) The Mengeles and their pals are so well established that since 1945 more or

85

less five hundred million mostly innocent people have been killed globally. No, not Jews. People. (Don't forget, Jews were not really people.) Thus, business is booming globally. Especially the killing business.

*   *   *

Let's go back to Israel and not forget that all above I am writing for you, for the sake of Israel's young generation from whom all this truth has been hidden ("Pa, how much will we get for Grandma and Grandpa"?!) The young and second generation hadn't a clue what that small child's question meant.[*] Thus I must clarify this crystal clear or we will grow generations of amoral psychopaths by no fault of their own. Then you will see for yourselves (we will look together) if we can get back on track (describe the high school visits to Birkenau-Auschwitz*—I quote the *Globe and Mail* report: "After the three minutes silent visit to the gas chambers and the ovens with ashes there followed an all-night good time in the discotheque with play girls.

Warburg bought IGFarbn cyanide division after the war. Because now, as I am writing these lines, I am not sure if it is the right thing to do, to return you back to become humane again, I am not sure as yet how to reconcile justice and morality with our past several generations of misleaders accounts.

*   *   *

*Segev, p. 488.

It's Friday afternoon before Shabbat, and, as usual I am alone, thinking vaguely. Thinking of the Lord. For thinking of Him clearly requires more than the ordinary man I am.

I am smaller than the ant and have less strength, for she is part of a community with great willpower and capacity to do and accomplish things, while I look up from amidst the tall, very tall grass blades and can barely see the pale blue of the sky, and even less so reach for Heaven, where God resides and looks down upon me, little ant Lee in the grass.

No: I am not praying: I am silenced mute from so much pain I can't tell one blade from the other.

I am reading Higham's *Trading with the Enemy,* and I see constantly before me the refuse, of my glorious holy people, the Baruchs, Morgenthaus, Einsteins, grinning sheepishly and crawling before FDR, who is puffing on his cigarette, sticking up high while the chimneys of Birkenau were puffing the souls of my children into the sky.

The three dwarfs submitting halfhearted, insincere petitions to the large towering president—about their brethren, of whom they were really embarrassed (and so was the entire American Jewish community)—for their brothers were poor. And what if the giant changed his mind and let them rescue their brothers? What will they do with 7 million poor relatives in front of their porches?! Oi!

So the towering giant knew "his little Jews," and to everyone's relief, threw the petitions into the wastebasket and winked to the other guy across the ocean: "Ady, mein boy, turn on the gas and do not worry. Leave it to me."

Yes, the American State Department and the American presidents were the main culprits of the Holocaust. That's why they could not let a single Jew land on their shores or in Israel. That's why they would not bomb Auschwitz and other extermination caps for "technical reasons."

*   *   *

From deep, deep subconscious and great distances, very great distances, my thoughts come from so far away that I did not believe lately anymore that they will ever come, they were so mute. I despaired of my Lord in me already.

This has become a dark continent now, for her counsellors have lost their minds. They are blind with no vision whatsoever and don't dare to move. An Egyptian darkness has set upon them.

The Kremlin wants Armageddon upon the West. The West wants Armageddon upon the Kremlin. Perhaps they both should succeed?

My heart contracts over its empty chambers. It is void and I no longer feel any fear or anger. The world has covered the traces of the victims. What has remained is a world of killers. January 18/45. To set the world straight, I will need to eradicate the root of an evil much greater and deeper than Hitler and Nazism. I will need to uproot the evil and carelessness of my nation's shepherds who let Nazism do to us as it did. Intellectuals, thinkers, poets, Chachmei Wilno and Lublin, the rebbes and scientists, Einstein, Oppenheimer, and all the Jewish Nobel Prize winners for science, wisdom and literature. Morgenthau, B. Baruch, F. Frankfurter, S. Wise, all made Hitler possible.

88

*   *   *

It is the second day of Shavuoth (Pentecost) and I am in the Bet Tzedek desperately trying to do some praying for all concerned, to no avail. Of course it's 36 years to this day I stood before the pillar of fire I did not understand. All the Earth was silent, the conscience of all men and my brothers, and that of the Lord, too. He sits on his throne, surrounded by Seraphim and ascending echo of shouts "Shema Israel" of those about to enter the flames rise to join Him.

Today it is just the same cloud 36 years later. I wander alone in the pillar of darkness, lost with the unknown behind me. The pain is unbearable. And as nothing wants to tally up, I decide to enter the thick cloud. I enter the thicket of my prayer book, and devour it leaf by leaf, and not much thought to it, for, in the end, what difference will it make what portion of the prayers enters me and in what order?! They all will wind up in those contorted convolutions of the brain and from there through the bloodstream rise to my parched mind surface and make a mist, I proceed on to the next leaf and the next while in deep thought about the Lord. Who knows what He thinks about this Lee and his doings?

The clearing in that forest is in a shroud until all the smoke disperses and I stand there all alone again. Naked as truth stands my white body, visible from afar.

Very shortly the holy days will come to pass and I am asked whether I'll go to the synagogue. I look at the stranger for a long minute, mute. No, I say after a while. For that synagogue would be that clearing in the forest, and I would call the Lord to come there too. And since all my thoughts and memories are gone now with the smoke up into the sky, it must be He in Heaven who got them now, for they must have entered Him to dwell there. Imagine now how the Lord feels with the knowledge of my thoughts and my memories, and what would His response be should He come to the synagogue on that clearing in the forest? If I should go to the synagogue and pray and call the Lord out, can you think what He would say to answer me?!

"No!!! No!!! My Lord don't come! No, don't come! Don't do it, don't do it my Lord! For then there will be no Heavens left, no sky, no forest, no trees, not even a blade of grass will be left on Earth to say to you a prayer to acknowledge Thee. For all will be ashes floating in the sky; and over whom will Ye be Lord then?! There would be no abode for Him if I went to the synagogue. There would be no Heaven and no Earth left, if I read out to Him the long litany of His transgressions. Yes, I carry all the generations of Israel past and future and my body and my soul ache painfully.

I visit my Holy Israel and I feel wretched. I feel very wretched, for my eyes have become blind and I see not my people out of despair and misery. See, my Lord, I beg you. Evil has surrounded me. The cab drivers are "achzarim," mean and brutal, the real estate dealers and government clerks, the noblemen (Mr. Rupin, Mr. Borochov) and the holy men . . . are all concerned with themselves and nothing but themselves.

What hits me like a rock is the nation's tremendous economic prosperity. A boom more virulent or at least most conspicuous than the boom of Canada or the U.S.A. All this on the strength of the merit and expense of the reparations for the dead and the exterminated. Without revulsion those reparations are accepted with the conscience of a cold-blooded Nazi murderer. There is a tacit unperturbed gaze on the face of the whole nation. They all know it, the low and the high, that they are eating from the spoils of their own dead. I have not heard one voice saying a mourning prayer for the dead. This applies to the religious, the irreligious, the literate and illiterate. If I intimate a remark in the direction of that line I am cut off by an attack, or by a cynical "What can you do." Expression of appeasement. They were appeasing me not to get upset, that they were not upset over the loss of their families. "It was quite a profitable loss, after all."

This reminds me of the scenes when transports left for the gas chambers; those left alive paid not a thought to that part of the reality of the event of the just past minutes ago and occupied themselves entirely with the leftover spoils and worldly possessions of the victims to be murdered in minutes. The psychiatrists of our time hasten to assure us, that this is quite all right, and necessary sublimation, substitution, or God knows, what term they use in order to overcome, such a shock, unhurt. "Very healthy" "Aby gesund." My speechless amazement is too long and I get a jolly slap on my shoulder. What is it? You worry about the past and the dead and the moral?! Did you not get a slice of the good times?!

My fellow prisoners turn away, laughing, to dispel their fear and embarrassment. The psychiatrists hasten to assure us that it is very healthy and quite all right, "thanks God," that they have overcome the shock unhurt coping with the post-traumatic stage exquisitely. These assuring medical terms are just perfectly suited to the leadership of my nation who need to defend themselves.

My friends urge me to write a book of redemption for them. But my response is numb: your five billion soul brothers need a weeding out. Then only will they be able to offer their hearts on the outstretched palms of their hands to make good.

The power of prayer and "wishing" are gone. The true believer in the power of prayer is non-existent. I will say the prayer and my wish will come true. The (Cohen) priest will bless me and I will be blessed. There are no more great rabbis to create reality ex-nihilo. The ability to transcend to "over there" no longer exists. The power of the rebbe to bless has no effect in our time, for no one believes in the power of the word any more. The jeshivas appeal to the brain only, and do not touch the heart. Why not? Because you all compromised with the enemy and the letter of the law. Our community leaders, in our weak presence, covered up innocent blood and larceny. Now this blood cries out of the earth and won't let you sleep. It causes your disbelief in decency and in yourselves. This is the cause of our misfortune. Compromising with our enemies. The great Belzer Rebbe had himself rescued from the fire and let his eleven children and wife burn in Belzec, 12 km from his house. The Chazon Ish did not raise his voice even with a peep against the ruling traitors. The Lubavitcher calendar 1940–41–42–43–44 has not a word on the Holocaust, not a single Kaddish!!!—for Wilno, Bialystok, Radom, Kielce, Bochnia, Lublin, Warsaw, Tarnow, Tarnopol and countless other Tarnows and Tarnopols.

The God of Sacrifice was invented by early man to terrorize the populace. The terror and brutality are man made. Not an Aztec god swallowed my seven million children. My own traitors did.

I will not play on man's heart and mind. The guilty and the insolent must stand naked in front of themselves and shrink. Read and hear, but pay no attention to the words lest they mislead you and corrupt your heart and senses. Let the words enter your innards and be absorbed by them and contort you with pain and repentance and echo back the desperately needed love from within, soothing and consoling that all of you are starved for, and stop the blood and heal the wounds that gape at us like giant abysses here to swallow us.

(I'm so jealous of JC: "This bread is my body, this wine is my blood." This is a time of famine. It's not a famine for bread, but a famine for the spirit of the Word of the Lord. "Ingest the wafer and I will enter your body, drink the wine and I will enter your blood and your mind.")

$$* \quad * \quad *$$

I walk slowly in the daylight air, sunshine and cosmic energy penetrate my dried-up flesh and skin. I feel myself resurrecting. That's how resurrection will come to the dead of the future, when a new spirit will enter them, cover their bones with new flesh and they will all prophesy.

Like the late summer fruit in the afternoon sun did I ripen, soaking up the anger and the hatred of all those who do not want to hear about themselves. They gave up their poison to poison me in turn. If you would lick my heart, it would poison you indeed. If you get down into the bowels of this book and let the pain penetrate your body and your bloodstream, you'll understand suddenly what ails the people and the Lord, what the problems are, where the hunger lies, the thirst, the sorrow and all else that tortures mankind, and **you** will bring forth the remedy.

Lest I send you a messenger again, the bearer of good tidings, who shall stand in front of you at the altar of glowing coals, touch his lips repeatedly until he stutters and utters not one word while you all shout at one another Holy, Holy, Holy, Sieg Heil! You will take your ploughshares then and beat them into spears and your pruning hooks into swords, and eat one another alive.

No, my Lord. That's not what You want. We both, You and I desperately want to cause a new spirit to enter our people, and remove the heart of stone that is in their chest now and put a heart of flesh in its place, and cause them to walk righteously. A new spirit enter you and compassion that will make you invincibly strong. No, not the tanks and the airplanes. You will become powerful. Your thoughts will have the power of long ago to will, to bless and create new realities and make visions become true again.

Isaiah and Malachi wrote in the "beautiful tongue" but failed to penetrate the people. If I just write beautifully, I, too, will lose you. I must enter your mind and body and bring forth out of **you** the Word of the Lord. Only then will you salvage yourselves.

Man fears silence, as he fears solitude, because it gives him a glimpse of the world of the hereafter. I cannot stand this planet and walk my inner space within, and the far outer spaces of Antarctica, Neptune, and Infinity. I sometimes meet myself and the purpose is elusive. How do I describe it? I desperately call the faraway earth from distant interstellar space, but my hope for a response is very faint. What did they (our misleaders) do to my people? They've dissolved in a mist over Birkenau, Majdanek, Treblinka, Belzec, Sobibor. I am here, but my reality is at another place where all my people went and you cannot fathom.

I'm an old man now, and my collected thoughts are scattered in the wind on so many scraps of paper. I need the strength and determination of Elijah to gird my loins with immense energy, to get back all my thoughts out of the whirlwind and order them anew upon a clean scroll, from where all the letters written with glowing coal will fire up, burn into the souls of all of you, scorch your minds with love and spirit of holiness, and make you come out possessed with rage to right the wrongs. Meantime, my scattered papers are still held by the wind, and I try to gather them all, one by one.

We Jews come from thousands of years back, searching for the visions we are haunted by, for our Holy People to be born. We went under and were reborn again with the burden of the past to carry forward millennia into the distant future. So we carry within our entire memory. It's hard, very hard and heavy burden.

*   *   *

Every last drop of pain and the piercing screams of every victim are all in me now, and every one of their curses are gathering like clouds of a storm that is upon you and you do not notice. All you united murderers will be paying with the lives of your children and the next generation which will not come to life, for you failed to weed out the Ben Gurions, Weizmans, Katznelsons, Borochows, Pereses, Dayans, Bubers, and their heirs and their contemporary ilk, and get them out from your midst now. If you doubt what I just said:—Listen then to the cry circling the Van Allen Belt that holds with an iron grip the communal brains of all humanity who sacrificed their friends, neighbors and even their very dearest on the altars of the modern Molochs you worship.

*   *   *

2,000 years our learned rabbbis talked to God and to themselves, but the People and the Land they ignored heartlessly. Prayers, repetitious ad nauseam, monologues and dialogues to a God in outer space. They produced thousands of volumes of vain, empty words. Even the regular massacres by the gentile populace surrounding them they endured. **Israel** was literally extra-planetary outer space to them since the last Bar Kochba (relatively simple folks) to the present date.

Not a single theologian of this enlightened 20th century, Jewish, Tao, Buddhist, Hindu, Muslim, Christian, has addressed himself honestly to the question of God. They all agree: He cannot be defined, so deep down in our conscience we and they are now all disbelievers. Nevertheless, we wrap ourselves in prayer shawls or other trappings and mumbo-jumbo recite 10–100 prayers. To whom? What? So, since no one is really looking inside our heart and conscience, why do we need any conscience? We can be inconsiderate, ruthless, brutal, murderous to no end.

No. We really cannot be that way, but we are, and our conscience is not even bothered. Thus our chosen rulers do whatever they please, and we comply with whatever they do without protest, and become their partners and victims at the same time.

You do not believe in any God at all. One who could, yes, mete out justice to transgressors after all. Our minds are confused entirely on all subjects: politics, economics, family. The earth is wealthier than ever and nine-tenths of humanity is starving. The Ten Commandments helped us come through millennia. We are now in front of an abyss. Darkness covers the sky. An Egyptian darkness has enveloped our rabbis, thinkers, philosophers, writers, scientists, and judges, dispensers of justice and righteousness. Our misleaders are killing us. And the same

96

evil spirits beset the gentile misleaders who did and continue to do even worse to their own nations.

*   *   *

The first thing that happens when a nation goes under is that its soul expires. It leaves the body virtually, the heart, the mind. The Soul? Leave the body of a nation? That's when and how a nation dies! No? Yes?

The writers, the poets, the aleph bet teachers and those who have taught us to connect our inner with the outer space and back with ourselves all leave. They leave. They become communists, atheists or some other new fashionable nihilists. The Talmudic scholars, too, who grounded our life, leave into the void. The old baalei tefila* die. The thousand-year-old nusach** and chants die with them. The soul that resided more or less where the thoughts molded by millennia of agonies to assure that the heart be right have simply evaporated. Life has suddenly become much easier. No worries, no anxieties, no fears. "Anything goes." Oh, yes! All feels very wonderful. The jazz, the new age and all the love! And lovemaking. Oh Lord! It's so wonderful. You don't even know with whom or why. It's unpremeditated, it's really spontaneous and wonderful. You suddenly feel like a God! You actually are God just then. You even create. You are a creator, a Lord, a God. Should I repeat it here in brackets? (Perhaps all this happens thanks to all those Wiedergutmachng monies of ten victims for each good Zionist Jishuvniks, and hora dancers.)

*Liturgical chant leaders
**Liturgical chants

97

Many pages of our history read pretty grimly: The exodus from Egypt was not very voluntary. The destruction of the ten tribes was a hair-raising tragedy. The first and second temples were not destroyed by Babylon and Rome. We did it! Infighting constantly. I am in Rome at the Coliseum, and my friend Mgungu is appalled at the story I tell her: The infamous Caesar, Nero and Calligula, threw to the lions daily a few men for entertainment of the crowds. In Viet Nam they threw thousands of times more people to napalm, and we are in the 20th century now! I will not go to Niniveh. Send the fish to swallow me and order it not to spit me out on the shore.

*   *   *

The 50th anniversary of Auschwitz and my thoughts come to me flying out of the clouds like freshly laundered bed   sheets   that   blow   in   the   wind: in 1939–40–41–42–43–44 the secrets were no secrets. All was known and my brothers in Canada and USA were strutting the industrial districts, each in his city, to the uniform and shoe factories, death factories past the newspaper headlines, to CIL, Dupont, Massey Harris, De Havilland Boeing, Lockheed, Northrop, G.M. G.E. for fat, fat pay cheques on Friday on the way to the liquor and beer stores. "To hell with those whining brothers, give me another piece of this good gefilte fish!"

*   *   *

The heavens rain tears, for there is no compassion. I am listening to the desperate sounds of the Talmudic stu-

98

dent that was myself 70 years ago, white, pale, swaying to the old nusach.* There is no remedy for my pain. The pain has become my nourishment. My cry is unbearable, for it is the cry and pain of all the future that I endure now. To sway the mind you must emit more sequences of such tone and wavelength that will sway the heart. Then the collective human heart will turn and command your rulers who usurp you to do the right thing.

I had a dream, a nightmare of a dream. On the Treblinka railway platform I meet a 7-foot tall SS man like Wirth who gives me a small silver rhomboid and says: "You can choose and rescue from here one Jewish person. One only." So, as Paul Reichman and his counterpart today appear passing by accompanied by a Saudi prince, I stop him and he just shrugs his shoulders: the extermination of his people is none of his business. He is mainly in construction business, and that's why he is allied with the Saudi prince, whose entire plan supports the extermination business.

*   *   *

Fear nothing and be ambitious! Raise your head high up! Get rid of the mental dwarfs who terrorize you with God commandments they don't believe in. Masochistic bearded cripples, non-leaders, get rid of them with your bare hands. Or a baseball bat or a kitchen chair leg. All the factions must unite for a common goal. We all must unite against our enemies that rule and oppress us. Their system is saddled upon us to malfunction.

*Liturgical chants

Lord in heaven, have compassion: How do I reconcile the past with the future? Those who died unjustly and the present generation who did not cause their death, are despaired over the sins of their fathers and desperately long for forgiveness. There are sins big enough that can coax the Messiah to come. We made a covenant with ourselves on Sinai onto all future generations. Our own brothers betrayed us in Birkenau. Our own leaders shipped us there and failed us.

The ancient prophets were desperate to bring redemption upon their penitent fellow men. But I am no prophet, I'm just like one of you, an ordinary man. I refuse to hold out hope to you, unless you rip out your usurpers from amidst you and have them pay off their debts first, or else be dead. Our prophets were very literate, their logic and language unsurpassable but failed the people every time. They talked to God back and forth but failed in their endeavors hopelessly. Imagine a contemporary Isaiah, George Will or Paul Johnson telling Clinton that Monica is a bad thing, or that selling high-tech to the Chinese is bad. The voters would kill their congressman if they stopped their Friday paycheques.

*   *   *

Letter to that rabbi of Eitz Chaim.

You were a young boy, but understood, just like your father and his contemporaries did, and pretended to be busy praying in their kaftans (to hell with January 18[*]). Now, thank God, that all our brothers are safely in the ov-

*The date they liquidated Auschwitz Birkenau with 250,000 inmates.

ens, they will not come to your door with hungry seven or eight little kinderlach (children), all is well. You got fat on profits during the war, and so you built majestic synagogues (tax refundable), and contributed to build Israel as well. You can now cheat God 100 percent. The out-of-faith marriages are 60 percent—Israel is being sold out again. So now, when I test that dot in the centre of your trefe heart about January 18, you know why the world is as it is. Because your bearded hypocrites got fat on Wiedergutmachung money after the war, you recurred to the almighty Catholic principle: just put on the tefillin, eat kosher, and believe. All will be well. And you drive the Porsches, BMWs, Mercedes, and Volkswagens. Most synagogue parking lots are at least half full of them. That's why even now the U.S., GB, most of Europe dare raise their fists and voices against us and support our mortal enemies.

Dear Rabbi of Dukla:

I just came back from the world of gestern (yesterday): Warsaw, Belzec, Sobibor, Majdanek, Treblinka, Rymanow, and Zabrod. No. Not one Jew is left. I did not come to ask why did the rabbis of Belz, Lubavich or the Chazon Ish not peep one word or incite to arms the nation and rise against all our killers and Israeli and American Jewish traitors.

Why did these three hunchbacked mental cripples not don sackcloth with ashes and lie across Dizingoff Street to let the buses run over them? I do not ask why the Mapai psychopaths, Weitzman, Ben Gurion, and Begin betrayed us, why our foremost scientists (Einstein, Oppenheimer and thinkers Achad Haam, Leibowitz (you can list 10 more names), and writers betrayed us. All above are amoral scum with no conscience.

Our current misleaders and traitors are selling the

nation again and leading us into the sea! Into the sea of fire, into a final holocaust that will consume world Jewry as well. The leaders all have Cessnas in their courtyards to fly them to safety, to Greece, Cyprus, etc. They don't know that they will be the last batch to be led to the execution pits when they have buried all their brothers. The Arabs, intifada stone throwers, fire bombers, and machine gunners, friendly neighbors, police of the PA authority, armed and equipped by Israel and the Chairman Jassir Araft, will finish them off mercilessly. Hitler was a kitten compared with Arafat.

You are an old, learned man, rise up and rouse the nation to revolt against our current traitors. Make the people who are desperate call for leaders who will make them act righteously.

*   *   *

The U.S. and Israeli Jewish leadership connived in 1933–39, together with the European, British, German, U.S. and Soviet rulers, to "solve" the Jewish problem and because the British (ARAMCO) did not know what to do with 7 million poor caftaned Jews with beards and sidelocks and hunchbacks with many children, babies, and elders, coming to Israel and face the Arabs as well?! Hitler was just doing the dirty work for all the European nations with the tacit approval of all concerned and the silent agreement with the Vatican and the world Zionist leadership, Israel Zionist leadership, traitors who promised "not to look." And, indeed, they never did. In 1941 the first refugee came, telling of the Jews gassed in Chelmno. And in 1942 Israeli returnees told of the Warsaw ghetto, Treblinka, Majdanek, Lublin, and other extermination places, and the Histadrut Mafia (read Mapai) shelved the reports. Not even in the spring of 1944, when Himmler and Eichman came and offered to sell the last one million Jews for five dollars apiece and a hundred Jewish millionaires refused to buy a live brother for the price of a chicken to rescue him from the pyres. Weissmandel and Joel Brand brought the German offer several times to the world and Israeli leadership. There was no taker. Our misleaders lured Joel Brand to Istanbul and Tel Aviv and handed him over to the British and shut him up. There was no taker for the price of one or two chickens, one life adult Jew, or child, or father, or grandmother.

This offer passed Roosevelt's, Churchill's, and Stalin's desks, and all three patriarchs of humanity refused to hear all this. They saw Jan Karski, who photographed Belzec and Warsaw and ignored him.

In 1944 Baruch, Morgenthau, Cohen, Frankfurter, Wise, all went to see FDR. He read their thoughts as clear as the skies. "Shema Israel! Mr. President, what will we do with one million naked relatives on our doorsteps?! Gevalt!" FDR emitted a satisfied patriarchal grunt: "Ady mein boy, turn on the gas!"

If Einstein, Oppenheimer, Fermi, the nearly all-Jewish team that held in their hands the future of the U.S. atom bomb project, would have put FDR on notice: "Stop the Jew-killing or we will not come Monday to our labs and offices," the killings would have stopped.

If the Americans would have but threatened the Germans with a pretend, feigned execution of their war prisoners, the Jew-killing would have stopped or slowed down at least. And now our current traitors and misleaders are leading the second batch of six million Jews into the sea.

The top dogs in Tel Aviv and Washington have mandated their men now again to arrange a destruction scenario that will pass unnoticed on the way to self-destruction.

The heirs of Roosevelt are already supervising "our security" from Arafat's territory. Israel let the U.S. build an airport and seaport near Gaza so the U.S. can airlift unlimited weaponry day and night to them. An entire division of CIA "peacekeepers" are there already and keep the foothold for a U.S. landing force, lest even a single Jew try to salvage himself from the Arab cutthroats.

The leadership of the small, strong state of Israel has organized itself on the U.S. military-industrial complex model in order to have its economy booming steadily. The people are blinded by this improved "economy," with their army generals in charge as executives and board members and partners in this wealth, with the oligarchy of numbered families, "The Nomenclatura." Our misleaders are now feeding our sworn enemies and strengthening them to fight us militarily to maintain our "economic system"?! That Rabin and Arafat handshake with the President of America meant war to be perpetual, and for everyone to be well off. The Jewish victims will be replaced by appeals for new immigrants to be slaughtered later for the U.S. Aztec gods. That's why the government of Israel established a slush fund for Arafat of 900 million dollars, and the Americans have delivered billions to him by now! The Israeli government knows that the Arabs are proxies groomed by the U.S. and UN Judenfressers to finish us off where Hitler fell short. Arafat's big helicopter, with the distinguished insignia supplied by the U.S. travels back and forth several times daily between Jericho and Gaza, loaded with most advanced special weapons, sting missiles, and anti-tank weapons.

What have we got to dialogue with Palestinians, Bed-

ouin migrants from Arabia? For every one intifada attack, collect all the adults of the entire village and make
them build our dividing security wall. And when they are
finished, put them on the other side of the wall and let
them march to Jordan, Lebanon, Syria, or Saudi Arabia.
Let them go back home where they came from originally
and where they belong. We have nothing to discuss or dialogue about with our mortal enemies.

*   *   *

BG, Weitzman, Usishkin, Rupin bought our own
land. BG, Peres, and Begin betrayed and sold our Land.
Einstein, Wise, Baruch, Morgenthau, Buber, Magnes,
Achad Haam, Leibowitz, Frankfurter did nothing for us
at the time they were needed. Their names should be
wiped off every street and plaza. From every memory
book their names should be wiped out. Our misleaders
who delivered us to them then and their heirs and successors now, who play ball with the U.S. and other "political
powers" or "economic interests" should be brought to ac-
count for their crimes. The Bormans, Eichmans and
Mengeles are second-rate criminals by comparison. In
1940–41–42–43–44 The Belzer, the Chazon Ish, and the
Lubavitcher did not do a thing about the murder of our
people in broad daylight. The ate fish and sang zmirot on
Friday eve. The Kibbutzniks danced the horahs. The Israeli people did not protest, and did not take a stand. All
the theatres were open, playing Pagliacci and Pinocchio.
The Vaad Rabanut approved all cinemas open and grand
Purim balls going on while my children were run into
pyres of Birkenau alive! The heirs of Goring, Borman, and
Mengele visit each other's estates in Ferraris. Why is my
nation hypnotized, blindly obedient to their treacher-

105

ous misleaders and destroyers? Why do we not have one Malcolm X, Farrakhan, Cleaver, Jackson, or Fanon. We call our leading destroyers chachamim unvonim, wise and understanding.

The chief Rabbi of Israel Yehuda Kook, referring to the Holocaust (quotes in some perverted manner outright from Ezekiel), "The spilled blood of the 6 million," the rabbi said, "was indeed horrible, but God's people had become so contaminated with the impurity of other nations that it was necessary to remove it with their own blood." (*(I am quoting verbatim from page 485 of T. Segev's The Seventh Million.)*

*   *   *

The Lord of Justice is a myth. When we were murdered during the first and second temple He was busy on Neptune and Uranus with mega projects. In Belzec, Sobibor, Treblinka, Majdanek, Birkenau, where was the Lord? Busy again? The misleaders of our time are out to kill us now. Where will the Lord be when we need Him next time?!

We are heading for our own funeral again: in Egypt the twelve clans pulled in twelve different directions. Soon after the monarchy was established, the twelve clans pulled in more different directions. Not the Babylonians or the Romans defeated us but the constant dissidy of the leaders of the time dug our graves. So, do now, the thirty-three parties bicker and pull in separate directions. Our newspaper writers are dead as well. Winston, Beres, Adelson, Eidelberg, great analysts of political reality! No! They write about extra-planetary news! How bad things are with the Arabs, the Israelis and the U.S., etc. Why don't you wake up and your readers also, before they

106

are buried live. I should pray to the Lord to arouse his wrath upon you, all who are giving us away to the five billion cannibals who want to devour my people all over again.

The Heavens rain tears. The land is desolate. There is no compassion and no consideration among men. The holocaust of my people would have never occurred if it was not for my traitors. Our left-wing traitors are cheating you: "We will provide security and peace." Our right wing says: "We will provide peace and security." The NRP care only about themselves and would sell their mothers two times over, and all of Israel and play games with the left and the right and are out of their minds regarding the reality of the Arab-Israeli conflict. Jeshivat Haraaion Haiehudi are full of hot air. To defeat your current destroyers you must strip naked their predecessors who pushed your parents into the gas chambers and made them into soap and fertilizers, then took the money for it. (The Bronfmans took the gold fillings and Swiss deposits when they knew that all possible heirs were safely dead.) How did you permit BG, Weitzman, Goldman, negotiate with UN, U.S. and GB about our Land?!—So we are negotiating ever since with them and with the Arabs.

*   *   *

Our Arab enemies have thousands of volunteers to take back our Land. We have echelons of Jewish beggar organizations! Oh! How good those British smell!! We have kumzits hemorrhoid kwetschers. Lice crawling the cities of the globe, sucking blood money. The Lubavitcher perverts have a diamond dealership in every German city. Begin in his demented state embraced his brother Sadat and gave him 70 percent of our Land for "peace."

We have protesters on the Golan: "We will never give up!" We have protectors **in front** of the Knesset of our chaverim. "We will never give up." Marzel, Feigilin, Shmuel Sacket would all sell Israel at half price to get a padded chair for themselves in the Knesset. We have perfidious Kach men who would like to sell Israel for half price or less! Just give them the padded cushions under their seats in the Knesset and palatial dwellings with all the perks.

Do Kaunda, Kabilla, Gorilla let the U.S. meddle in their internal problems? What is this? Why did the U.S. Pres, Vice-Pres, head if CIA, Sharon, King Huss, come to Camp David to see how many Jews we offer them to be killed? The U.S. death industry is in crisis. Texas and California are in crisis. No one wants to buy arms, even for nothing. Clinton sold China the most sensitive space armaments to give them strength and encouragement to come out for a super WW III.

*　　*　　*

It really was the U.S. people's economic resurrection by sending Hitler dollars and goods via the Bank of International Settlements. Basel, NY, Paris, Chase Manhattan, JP Morgan, etc. There were 1001 arrangements well documented in many books such as, *Trading with the Enemy* by Higham.

Fifty years too late there are piles of evidence that the Swiss knew the gold bars they were getting from the Germans for war goods, payments or just safe keeping in their vaults, were the dental fillings of the gassed Jews. The U.S. knew it too. The Stuka planes shot down over England in 1942–43 had parts produced and labeled by the SKF Chicago 1942 and preferentially supplied to Germany over the needs of the U.S. and GB airforce.

You get up and cry out for the crimes of our previous gang of misleaders (you can name at least ten, BG, Weitzman, Remez, Eshkol, Dayan, Rabbin, Peres, etc.), and bring them to justice. Or else the guilt will be yours, if you let our current misleaders sell us to the U.S. now a second time. They are selling us out again. The U.S. and Israeli Jewish leadership connive together with the Americans again! Identify your misleaders. Count out their crimes loud and clear to our hypnotized nation.

We must draft a new dictionary and a new language. The fictitious history, written by the founders of Israel, has to be rewritten all over again. We must get rid of those Sodomites.

How did the people permit BG, Weizman and Goldman to represent us? Represent us in some UN assembly? Assembly of who?! Assembly of our United assassins, and negotiate about our Land? With the UN? With Waldheim? A former gestapo man and now twice president of this den of iniquity? In 1945–48 our misleaders were "negotiating" to repossess our Land?! We could not beat the British with kitchen knives and clubs?—Sure, then we needed to "negotiate." But since the US president and his cohorts knew the Jewish traitors who shoved their brothers into Hitler's ovens just three to four years earlier, they negotiated with them accordingly. And we have been negotiating with our archenemies ever since! We are sucking money from them giving them our best youths' blood in exchange.

*   *   *

The October 1973 War was not a "surprise." The Israeli government pre-arranged the Yom Kippur war,
planned for the Egyptians "to restore their wounded national pride."

That traitor Bar Lev, a general, built a Potemkin
wall instead of real defense line and smuggled the money
for it to Switzerland.

Hebron was ours. Netanyahu made a Hebron agree-
ment with the Bedouin nomads and gave up 80 percent of
Hebron. Abu Hitler is Hebron's chief of police now. Abu
Tabuk, the infitada executioner. What right did
Netanyahu have to make a Hebron agreement?!

For 2,000 years our "leaders" of the past, and those
now did not make a claim for the land of Abraham, the
land of their forefathers, the land promised to us by God,
with borders well-described in the oldest book of deeds of
mankind written by God (or be it even by Abraham and
Moses for practical purpose, is irrelevant). The words of
the deed were registered 4,000 years ago, and Abraham's
descendants lived there ever since. He and our other patriarchs are buried in Hebron. Hebron is where David
was crowned King. And what is there to discuss about Jerusalem with anyone? Jerusalem is where our capital
was built 3,000 years ago, and King David was crowned
there and ruled with his successors afterwards for nearly
one thousand years! But there was not a single man who
passionately voiced our cause! I mentioned to you that I
had my reservations at Abraham's buying of the plot, the
Mearat Hamachpela from that Hittite peasant. For the
Lord told Abraham three times "this land is yours and
your children's forever." That's why we now dispute Hebron with the Arabs. I am not an admirer of King David,

110

and I am distraught at David's buying Aravna, the Jebusites threshing floor that is the Temple Mount where Isaac was offered to be sacrificed and subsequently the Holy of Holies was built.

Now imagine Begin meeting Sadat with a brotherly embrace. Sadat, who was Hitler's admirer. Sadat who, just a few weeks earlier, returned from Berchtensgaden, the Fuhrer's skiing resort. Where are the Jews? Where is Israel? In Camp David?

Like in the olden days, our own leaders dug our graves then just as these do now. Arik Sharon, our hero general prime minister now, and several of his predecessors permitted in the Gaza open market to buy dynamite sticks, hand grenades, bazookas, uzis, just as you buy vegetables. Then follow the Intifada murderous attacks on us. This insanity is called freedom, equal rights, democracy.

We are supposed to be the elect nation of the Lord, sons of princes and priests. Take a sober critical look onto the roots of the character of our present-day Erev Rav.[*] I am sitting Shiva and mourning fifty years for my brothers.

I want a Holy Spirit to descend upon you and make you invincible. (I told you, I love to be orthodox, just like people love tennis, parasailing or golf.) But I will not let myself be dictated to as what is orthodoxy by bearded hypocrites.

No one ever gave a single thought as to why, 2,000 years, an entire people across the globe, intelligent people, permitted themselves to be ruled by kaftaned mental

*Mixed multitudes

dwarfs, "dispensers of the word." They managed to stop reality for 2,000 years under the pretext of a redeemer Messiah to come. Even sages like Rashi and Rambam and great thinkers let themselves be deluded about a Messiah on a donkey.

Intellectuals, thinkers, educated men, no one permitted a caring, loving thought a mere tremor enter their heart or their mind. (What heart? What mind?!) A passion, a feeling, of love like you would feel for a woman, a child. A passion that would overwhelm them, rule them, were they in love with their Land. That is, if they were able to arouse such sentiments at all. They are not capable even of loving a dog or a pet, never mind a person and so much less their nation, unreasonably, passionately, and arise to action and retake **Our Land** for 2,000 years, and make claim to our property.

We were ousted from it by force. But that does not diminish the legitimacy of our ownership. All those who ousted us no longer exist. Wars were always customary and the weaker were vanquished. The conquerors were also vanquished a little later by new conquerors. The victims and the victors who struggled on that territory of ours all vanished, and none exist. We, the Jewish people who always owned that land, Israel, we alone exist and own it to date. We may have wandered, forced out from it, around the globe, but every day, even now, we stop three times, face the east and pray for our return to Jerusalem and Zion our Homeland.

They ousted us from Spain, too, as recently as 500 years ago and the streets of Cordoba, Grenada, Seville, and Salamanca still bear Jewish names. Hundreds of churches there are blatantly and shamelessly standing—obvious Jewish synagogues taken by force. The Jewish owners of their houses in Spain and Portugal hold the

112

keys of their homes to the present day. Even now, where we finally reached an age of enlightenment and law, the mighty still say they are right just because they possess the goods they robbed from us. Even the organized mafia would not get away with a thing like that if caught. Spanish, Portuguese, British, French, Italian and the Vatican museums and libraries, hold our Hebrew sacred books and priceless manuscripts.

They say shamelessly "our Hebrew books that we cannot even read are **their Hebrew books.**"

This blatant thievery, practiced without a pang of conscience against the Jews for centuries, caught up with the worldwide plunder of all the nations who rob one another even now and call themselves civilized on top of all this.

The World Jewish Organizations, the U.S. Jewish Organization, the Zionist Organization of all parties in Israel did not manage to save a single Jew from Europe, though they were clearly told in advance that all the Jews would be killed. The entire gentile world hated the Jews, it was so fashionable and later so profitable. They drew up a long list of good reasons why the Jews should be killed and no one needed to be blamed. This gentile world found a willing executioner who did the dirty job for them, and Europe became Judenrein finally. The setup was perfect. Everyone loved it. Even the world Jewish and Zionist leadership loved it. No more filthy, bearded, hunchbacked Yids in black kaftans.

As you will see further, there were some flaws in the planning. Not in the Jew-killing. That part was perfect and total. The flaws, not figured well in advance, were that from 1939 to 1945 the gentiles killed among each other 70 million non-Jews. (Did you hear the gentiles even do one-tenth of the amount of wailing or mourning, as we do for our seven million?!) Since 1945 to date, four to five hundred million more people have been killed. For a minute you will be inclined not to believe me. Well, keep the pages of your time event screen I set up for you at the beginning of this narrative and watch while I write.

Run at your current traitors and strangle them with your bare hands, for it is these scoundrels who have been strangling you all this entire time. Go on a rampage against every city hall and public official's residence and make an end to all of them. Call out to the people and get rid of the traitors at once! Within the hour! Chase them out of their plush residences and do away with them! And a new spirit shall rest upon you and make you invincible, and make you become a Man, humane again. Identify all the Jewish top Rumkowskis, exhume them and do away with them again and bury them. Hang their effigies over our people's mass grave in Poland and the Ukraine. Eradicate the bearded perverts and strip their masks off their faces and their kaftans. Make them walk naked the streets in broad daylight. Throughout the millennia they failed you in each historical crisis.

*　　*　　*

We must stop being a defense league, and become an offense league, to free ourselves of the poisoners of our people. A radical Jewish group should form a government in exile. After all, Israel belongs to all the Jews in the world. We all contributed blood and money to Israel's resurrection.

Such government should be on a territory where the largest number of Jews outside Israel lives. We must draft a short and clear memorandum that would outline the agenda of this government.

- The detailed draft of the constitution must be approved by plebiscite point by point, and before that book is closed every Jew should have the right to contribute.
- None of the infamy so painfully described on these pages should ever need to recur.
- A reformed direct electoral system contrary to the perversion that is structured in Israel today.
- Streamline the bureaucracy to one quarter of the current system.
- The legislative maze that oppresses the ordinary man today must be radically rectified.
- A judicial system independent of government politics.
- The state of affairs of our country and of our nation can easily be reversed. The entire system must be swept away. The legislative executive and judicial branches of the government must be separated. Israel must have a constitution that will make possible for the nation free elections that guarantee the right of referendum on any important issues of public concern. Just as they have in Switzerland and some states of the U.S. Thus, bureaucratic control and unjustified taxes can be held in check or reduced. Every citizen must have equal rights before the law.
- Israel economic system must be liberated from the control of bureaucrats, and the dictatorship of the 20 top families who have an iron grip on the entire economy, and must get their usurpers off their backs, for only then, and in no other way will Israel be able to function successfully as a country and as a nation.

115

- The top government appointments from President, Prime Minister, Cabinet Ministers must serve free of any renumeration.
- A brand new agenda must be drafted in regard to the ownership of our Homeland as outlined in the oldest book of deeds on earth—the bible—four thousand years ago. There can be no compromise on a single square foot of our Land. With no bedouin nomads as there were no such people ever as Palestinians nor a land of Palestine. That was all invention.
- We must not sell out or betray our national interest to anyone for any price, and thus regain the respect we lost or rather never had with the other nations of the world, who witnessed through the decades the treacherous behaviour of our own nation's misleaders.
- We must give notice to the assembly of the United Nations, that lest they revert to egalitarian civilized behaviour, we quit, and have nothing to do with them.

*   *   *

My text is purposeful all right, I tried to keep my language restrained. Yes: the text is intentionally liberal so that **you** determine its purpose yourself, and choose what will trigger you to action, to rectify and make good that urgently needs to be done.

This is your book now equally and not only mine.

Epilogue

Since there is not a single bearer of light amongst my people of Israel, darkness envelopes the earth. Darkness so thick that you cannot see at all. That's why all events of our time have befallen you and you have not noticed. Not the Jews alone do you oppress wishing their death. Most nations are at one another's throat right across the globe.

Ever since the first oligarchs of those darks ages you called enlightenment, to the very present day, 250 years, the most brutal usurpers of power rule over you with your consent. They all have the audacity to call themselves democrats as if they ruled in the name of the people. All those who rule you are dictators, socialists, communists, fascists, Nazis, who possess no mandate from Heaven, nor a mandate from you, the people.

Majesty is a prerogative that belongs to God solely, and from Him alone this glory emanates upon such who govern righteously His estate.

There is not one such ruler today. They're all tyrants who have no consideration for your lives, not even the lives of your small children who never sinned. Your rulers' power comes from the mansions they occupy, and bloats them with arrogance and cruelty. Their power comes from your strength.

Walk up, therefore, each one of you to the palaces they live in and demand accounts for their deeds and misdeeds and brutality. Walk up to them with baseball bats and broken off wooden chair legs and with your bare hands stop your killers and take away their power from the mayors and ministers and members of parliament who do not represent your needs and desires. Undo their power. Undo all of them.

Vacate the mansions from where their power emanates and move them to the hovels of your poor, and the poor, and the hungry move into those mansions that overflow with your wealth.

We are at the break of another major shift in our evolution. An era of development is still unfolding in this evolutionary shift. We all feel it emotionally and spiritually. After all, humanity is one soul group and we want new goals and a new way of life. The time is close at hand. We are entering an age of true enlightenment and compassion this time. We are entering unchartered waters. The key is, to gain greater insight as to your karmic connections to your fellow men and the earth herself. We must focus our attention to greater priorities of highest and best purpose.

How we understand and live the pleasure principle today versus the not too distant tomorrow will not be comparable with that of today. I will not explain in detail this, for it is beyond for what the human brain is currently designed for. In time, the new generation of human consciousness will have better insight into this, and this will be soon achieved. Life will be beautiful, happy, joyful, and all this will become reality. New life like there has never been before.

Choose from among yourselves honourable men who will, yes, serve you faithfully. Who will stand barefoot in front of you with their heads bent humbly before your Majesty, the People, the Lord.

Notes

From: *The Seventh Million* (T. Segev)

p 25—Jabotinski, Arlazaroff, Sam Cohen, Levi Eshkol, Ben Gurion Sharett, Rupin were bickering not over life and death of the near future victims, but how to get their paws on the Jekkes money.

p 25—Jabotinksi was negotiating, talking to Petlyura to train for him a Jewish gendarmerie.

p 23—Ahimeir lauded the Fuhrer, Mussolini, Ataturk, Pilsudski.

p 27—B.G. (In 1935): "The war against anti-Semitism is not a part of the Zionist mission."

p 29—The Jewish agency executive sent Hitler a telegram to his victory. The Zionist organization sent Hitler a condolence telegram on Hindenburgh's death.

pp 28–30—B.G. and A. Ruppin corresponded amicably with Baron Mildestein, Eichman's predecessor, and the Angriff cast a special medallion with a swastika and the star of David when Mildestein visited Palestine.

p 32—Arlasaroff visits Magda Goebels-Friedlander and the Nazis let the Betar wear brown shirts, britches, boots and belts all under Gestapo auspices.

p 33—The Irgun and Etzel or rather Lechi-Stern gang had contacts with Mussolini and German Nazis "to fight the British."

p 41—Mapai opposed illegal immigration because they taught themselves to be the "legal heirs" of the British administration.

p 43—Weitzman "how will the poor little land support these people?" Henrietta Szold: "We should send back the useless

119

immigrants." Eliahu Dobkin: "These Jeke refugees" are undesirable material. And indeed St. Louis was turned back from the shores of the United States back to Bremen in 1939 . . . to Auschwitz. Hitler: "Now you see! No one wants you! In the ovens!"

p 56—The Jishuv hated the Jekkes out of envy!

p 64—March 1943 at the height of extermination they sang and danced the horas, and went to the movies.

p 67—When Rommel threatened Israel the Mapai and Irgun leadership were trembling in their pants and planning to collaborate with the new occupiers.

p 74—Charkov Jews murdered. Half a million Jews of Romania exterminated—Haaretz page two. The soccer team won in Damascus is on page one.

p 74—Several dozen Jishuv Jews came back in November 42 and reported on Auschwitz—three furnaces etc. and Warsaw. This was point number six of the Jewish agencies agenda. The disputes of local factory management and workers took up all the rest of the session.

p 75—Frankfurter, Wise, Morgenthau, Baruch met already Karski etc.

p 76—Berel Katznelson of the Davar says that there is no demand for news of the Holocaust.

p 77—Haaretz on front page: Jewish children killed with rifle butts, and on the next page "Pagliacci" is advertised huge!

p 78—Haaretz March 1943: Three million Jews killed, but the Purim ball will be held anyway; "Pinocchio" in T.A. cinemas.

p 79—B.G. in 1943 "It's all there in the Mein Kampf, but Jews have a sadistic nature (sic) and, instead of seeking a solution they only try to find whom to blame."

p 80—In 1942–43 both the rabbinate and the secular perverts decided that the cinemas should stay open (just like the Lubavitsh perverts calendars reflect faithfully in the same tone.

p 82—B.G. in 1942: "The Holocaust should be treated as a natural disaster—It is not the Jewish agency's business to save the Jews of Europe but to build the Land of Israel." (Later we will grab the multi-billion Widergutmachung for the soap and fertilizer made of our brothers and build an even better Israel!!)

p 85—Between March 1941 and March 1944 the Hagana did not bring in a single refugee boat.

p 86—B.G. in 1943: "We need to advance the Zionist fundraising."

p 90—In October 1941 the Rumanians killed 130,000 Jews, 70,000 were still left and offered to go free for $200 a piece!—No takers.

pp 91–96—In January 1944 Wiesmandel, Gizi Fleishman—Joel Brand Story—Eichman, Wisliczeny-Himmler offered 1 million Jews for $200 apiece and then lowered the price to $5 per Jew.—Sally Meyer, Churchill, Roosevelt all refused!

p 97—In early 1943 a young woman arrived from Poland, Osviecim, Warsaw, Treblinka, Majdanek and B.G. personally interviewed her and said: "I am deeply disturbed, but you see the sun is rising in all its might and one must go on with one's own work" (verbatim)—finish.

p 98—B.G. "The disaster of Europe's Jews is not directly my business." Dov Josef asks the leading press unions not to write of the Holocaust for where could Israel find place to accommodate all those Jews.

p 99—J. Grunbaum: "We have been appointed to witness the death of 7 million Jews."

p 100—Berel Katznelson: "We could save maximum 10,000 Jews useful to Zionism for country building (children to grow in Mapai spirit, old party functionaries). To save a million would be a burden to us. You see German Jews brought money. These are all destitute."

pp 102–3—Jitzchak Grunbaum: "The Jishuv has one priority only: Zionism!" in 1939 they knew of the gassing of the Jews in vans in Chelmno, but the Mapai political committee refused to debate this. You could hear the victims pounding on the trucks' walls till their cries died. The Jewish agency was spending money buying land for new settlements. One Mapaink did protest, but the Davar refused to publish his speech.

p 105—All the papers protected the public from news on the Holocaust,—absolving thus their conscience. The entire Jew-

121

ish executive was in accord with B.G. The Holocaust at one executive meeting was number 6 of the agenda discussing 8 items, mostly union disputes and the May Day celebration.

p 109—Grunbaum 1943: "The Jews of Poland preferred life of a dog rather than death with honour."

p 113—Dobkin of the first arrivals: "At first I thought they were animals."

p 115—B.G. visits Bergen Belsen, "depressing"—and goes off to Frankfurt for antique book hunting.

pp 116–17—Dobkin has even a worse attitude "animals"—In the Russian sector of Berlin in a cellar 47 small live children were found, rats were gnawing at them. The U.S. army treats the survivors just as the Germans did, they just do not shoot them or gas them.

p 119—B.G. in 1945. "Most survivors are here because they were tough, selfish egotists and evil, else they would have not survived. And they are not necessarily the best for Israel!!"

p 119—The Jishuv who danced the Hora and sang and ate the five years needed these tough survivors for the coming war with the Arabs, so they let them come in "undesirable material" (six). Meir Jaari and Dobkin called them "scum" and "soap."

p 120—B.G. met with Eisenhower and proposed to him to concentrate all the survivors in Bavaria, and establish a temporary Jewish state there until they are fit to go to Israel.

p 129—B.G. in 1945: "It is the job of Zionism not to save even the Remnant of Israel, but rather to save the land of Israel for the Jishuv (so they could continue to dance the Hora and have the time of their lives). Eliahu Dobkin.

p 138—C. Jahil: "We have not declared that the Remnant and the land of Israel are one and the same, rather we emphasize that the Remnant must exert a great mental and physical effort to integrate with the Jishuv.

p 158—December 1944, Roza Korczak told a Shomer Hatzair kibbutz about Ponary: "When the bodies burned, a pregnant woman's abdomen exploded and expelled a fetus to burn with the mother."

p 159—To the Jishuv the new olim were—sabon—soap. The

122

kibbutznihim treated the alijat hanoar with brutality—sabon.

p 161—Very few families were willing to shelter new olim.

p 163—B.G. "I have no time to see immigrant absorptions! People can live in tents for years. If they don't want to, then let them not come here."

p 172—They would not let them go to ORT schools or higher education because then they would leave the kibbutz—Shmuel Dayan (father of the general) "What's so horrible about agriculture?! We are not sending them to Siberia after all!"

p 173—People arrived without anything, even a change of clothes—so that was their crime!

p 174—Kibbutzim refused old people, small children, sick people, or social problems.

p 175—Levi Eshkol: "Israel can not absorb all the crazy Jews of the world."

p 177—22,000 Holocaust survivors took part in the 1948 war. One of every three fighters. And one of three casualties was a Holocaust survivor!!

p 178—B.G. Through human debris in the enemy's eyes.—And on the bones of the boys from the Holocaust a new road to Jerusalem was built.

p 179—Jitzhak Sadeh famous Palmach commander encounters a woman soldier with a tattoo on her chest—FOR OFFICERS ONLY!—He is not impressed.

p 180—In December 1944 Roza Korczak heroine fighter of the Wilna ghetto was at a Histadrut convention to tell the facts. So B.G. complained "Comrad refugee is speaking in a foreign language, Yiddish." (see also page 158)

p 187—Elimelech, Rimalt, member of Knesset: "My little son came home last night and asked me,—how much will we get for grandma and granpa? (Who are sold as soap from the shelves of the grocery store, wrapped in paper with olive branch print.)

p 208—Five thousand Yemenite children were kidnapped from hospitals in Israel and sold for adoption.

p 238—Dov Shilanski tells of the end of his death march on April 29 in Bavaria: **Nearly all died.**

p 238—Jasha Heifetz comes to Israel and plays Richard Strauss pieces, so a good Betar man breaks his hands and fingers with an iron bar as well as his violin.

p 308—Johanan Ben Zakai recommended the surrender to Babylon.

p 311—Israel was selling to Germany arms.

p 314—Mapai central committee approved the sale. "There is no value to national pride! If the slaughtered millions could see from their graves or from heaven what is being done in Israel, even the selling of arms to Germans they would be very proud."

p 364—Buber, Bergman, Gershon Solem, Jehuda Bacon, Leah Goldberg and 17 others signed petitions to pardon Eichman. "He was a small cog in the entire German extermination machine that really was expressing the desire of the entire gentile world."

p 375—Now the French provide us with the best French helicopters. The German airforce trains Israeli pilots and Israeli officers train at German army officers schools. We have now a common law marriage with Germany. Israeli children go on exchange visits to Germany and vice versa.

p 379—When the German ambassador arrives in Israel the German national anthem was to be played. So Begin says, "Yes we should all get up and sing together, Deutchland, Deutchland, uber, alles." By the way, the Germans promised to set up their embassy in Jerusalem but they didn't.

p 400—De-Nur the author of Ka-Tztnik testifies at the Eichman trial he saw an SS man murder a boy who had been a victim of his sexual perversions. The soldier then grilled the boy's body on a spit and gulped down the meat piece by piece. De-Nur saw his sister Daniela among the camp prostitutes, and he saw his mother standing naked in line to the crematorium with all the others, and he saw them going up in smoke. "Mother I am with you always,—after all it is you and I, Mother: you and I and the terrible snow that will remain with us always."

p 401—In a dialogue between H. Rosenblum and Amos Oz in the Yediot Achronot, Rosenblum writes:

Arafat, were he only to get enough power, would do to us things that even Hitler never imagined. This is not rhetoric on our part. If Hitler killed us with certain re-

124

straint—were Arafat ever to come to power, he would not merely play at such matters. He would cut off our children's heads with a war shriek, rape our women in broad daylight before tearing them to shreds, and throw us off every roof into the street and skin us like hungry tigers in the jungle wherever he came across us, without German "order" and Eichmann's organized transports. . . . What did Begin do wrong in mentioning Adolf Hitler? Yes, that despot was a kitten compared to what Arafat will bring. . . . Begin did not exaggerate—in fact, he minimized—the danger lying in wait for us from the rise of this mass murderer from Beirut.

When considering the U.S. Secretary of State John Foster Dulles and Senator Joseph McCarthy the United States is a country of racial discrimination and lynch gangs, a danger to the Jewish people. "Treblinka could easily be reborn near New York and Majdanek near Chicago."

p 478—In 1966 and again in 1967, delegations of young people paid visits to the sites of the death camps in Poland. On their return they were quoted saying, "We left as Israelis and returned as Jews."

p 488—As they stood beside the death furnaces in the extermination camps, their hearts filled with resentment and tears they wept with pain and sorrow over the destruction. We are proud now as we see the flag of Israel flying high above the death pits and furnaces, we stand straight and proud. "The people of Israel live! We swear before our millions of murdered brothers: if we forget the old Jerusalem let my hand wither." By the time they reached Auschwitz, they had no tears left.

Two or three hours later after returning from visiting the death camps they were dancing at discos with young Polish strippers.

*   *   *

125

From *The Struggle for the Soul of Israel* (J. Hazoni)

p 9—Buber, Leibowitz, Jeshaiahu: The concept of Jewish nationality was invented by Zionist politicians (to disinherit the indigenous inhabitants.)

p 12—We envision a state that will not be a nation state. (In 1997, the Dutch tourist guide book hopes that Holland will disappear from history.)

p 19—J. Elkana opposed all Holocaust awareness: Israeli leaders must remove this historical remembrance from our lives. Nationalism is a curse of the nations that dominates every part of Israeli life currently.

p 40—In 1930 the children of the founding labor families were the wealthy oligarchy and they removed the red flag symbol from their meetings and they stopped singing the internationale.

p 41—During Begin, Zuvulun Hammer of the national religious party and Shulamit Aloni started dejudaising Israel: The IDF texts stopped to contain God as reference, The flag to contain a halfmoon and change the text of the Hatikva during chief of staff and later Prime Minister Ehud Barak were set down 11 value points that deny connection between the Jewish people, the land of Israel. The concepts of Jewish or Zionist are all crossed out from the military code. Even the word Jewish state or Zionism were crossed out, for they are non democratic and nazistic.

pp 62–65—Shimon Peres (Perski) and Shulamit Aloni never went to university (Betshemen anti-Zionist school founded by a disciple of Martin Buber, Sigfried Lehman with Ben Gurion's approval:

The independent state is a recent invention. (Hugo Grotius introduced the concept of sovereignty in the 17th century.)

p 121—Samson Rafael Hirsch, Herman Adler, chief Rabbi of England, plus all the association of German Rabbis and the orthodox Rabbis and the central conference of American Rabbis all united in this statement: Jewish national state is contrary to the messianic prophecies of Judaism.

126

Rabbi Zvi Yehuda Kook, referring to the Holocaust (refers in some perverted manner outright to Ezekiel) **"The spilled blood of the 6 million the rabbi said, was indeed horrible, but God's people had become so contaminated with the impurity of other nations that it was necessary to remove it with bloodshed."** (This quote comes from page 485 of T. Segev's The Seventh Million.) Zionist Organization against Achad Haam and established the Mizrachi in 1902 as a second labor party.

p 133—In 1900 Zionist congress in London Hertzl rallied 41 members of the British parliament voting for Zionist Israel. He also succeeded to rally the Russians.

p 158—David Gruen born in Plonsk went to school only till age 13 and emigrated to Israel in 1906 and became a most efficient demagogue.

p 169—Britain obtained the mandate over Palestine in 1917. Balfour expressed himself favorably but not bindingly to establish and national home for Jews in Palestine. For administration of that territory a Jewish Agency was established.—On the Paris conference in 1919 and in the San Remo conference in 1920, Weitzman, now president of the Zionist organization, when asked at the allied council if what the Jews want is an independent autonomous government, Weitzman said NO. "We do not demand a specifically Jewish government, (we want a little state like Monaco with a University instead of a gambling casino!)"

p 197—Meantime Buber, Rupin, Hugo Bergman, rector of the university, Juda Magnes president of the university, Gershon Shalom, Norman Bentwitch the attorney general, Lord Samuel's son, the governor of the country, Henrietta Szold, Werner Senator (later Vice President) all wanted a Jewish-Arab peace association because the idea of establishing a sovereign power for the purpose of protecting the Jews is intrinsically immoral, illegitimate and anti-democratic.

p 204—Louis Marshall, the Warburgs, Buber, Werner Senator, and the entire Zionists executive in London in 1929, declared explicitly that the Jews have no intention turning the land of Israel into a Jewish state. Einstein, J. Magnes:

"We must give up once and for all the idea of a Jewish state unless we have the support of the Arab population. The publisher of New York times, Adolf Ochs,—a Jew—supported the same.

The Arabs responded promptly in March 1930 with multiple massacres of the Jewish population, in Jerusalem, Hebron, Zfat, that lasted 3 days and was staged by A. Husseini the chief Mufti of Jerusalem who was installed by Sir Herbert Samuel, Jewish governor of Palestine although he knew well that the Mufti had a 14-year sentence on him for previous massacres. **It was established by his commission that the Jews are guilty of being massacred because they did not convincingly renounce the Jewish state**—Buber and his group asked Amnesty and release of all the apprehended killers.

p 217—At the 17th Zionist congress in Basel, Weitzman recommended binationalism and renounced the Jewish state just when the pogroms in Poland went full blast. "A majority is not required to develop a Jewish civilization and culture"— nothing is said about a Jewish State in the Balfour declaration. The essence of Zionism is not a Jewish state, but the creation of material conditions for establishment of an autonomous production facility.

p 241—Meantime World War II broke out and the Jewish leadership had eyewitness accounts of gassing Jews in Chelmno. In 1941 photographs and eyewitness accounts were provided by the Soviets about mass exterminations in the Ukraine, Belarus, Birkenau, Aushwitz, Warsaw, Treblinka, Majdanek, Belzec, Sobibor.

p 257—Buber had a picture with a large cross hanging behind his desk. Magnes and his gang were against the establishment of a Jewish state because "We are abandoning Jewish Holiness for a totalitarian Zionist oppressive rule. Secularization cultivates thoughts and visions that keeps man from hearing the voice of the living God." The politisation of life strikes at the very spirit itself. Buber and friends ran petitions for pardon and clemency for Eichman.

p 263—On May 14th 1948, two labor leaders flew to ask Leon Blum in Paris if to declare a Jewish state.—Only 6 out of

128

ten of the assembled provisional government voted for an independent state, instead of trusteeship. So the very same day, 5/14/48, the shysters proclaimed the state of Israel.

p 272—In 1952 our beloved brothers suddenly remembered their 7 million murdered kin,—the entire Jewish people in the diaspora. They too were creators of the Jewish state and all that belonged to them now belongs to Israel. (Wiedergutmahung, will alles gut machen für uns.)

p 286—Buber's pupils went in a midnight torch light parade on his 85th birthday and garlanded him with flowers, kissed him, and made him an honorary member of the Student Union.

p 286—The Pharisees recognized wisely when the Romans destroyed us that there is really no need for a Jewish state. We outgrew that necessity in the year 70 BCE that the state and the stage of power are of much importance. The inner power of the mind turned the national catastrophe into a source of life, that is our power to the present day. We need legitimate power other than this.

p 291—Leibowitz: **The state is nothing but an apparatus for coercion and violence that exists for its own sake.** Heroism and courage on the battlefield cannot be considered a virtue.

p 303—What do the people in Tel Aviv have to do with the covenant of Abraham? Is the general chapter of the IDF some local chapter of the general staff of the Lord of Hosts?

p 310—Lavon just like Buber, did not want mass Jewish immigration from Arab lands, as they are of "poor quality."

p 327—Revivalism by 1973 as B.G. died was a total failure, since Israel by then was ran in all its departments by graduates of Buber and his similars.

Kadish
קדיש
(for the Seven Million)

Yit-gadal	יִתְגַּדַּל	*Birkenau*
ve-yit-kadash	וְיִתְקַדַּשׁ	*Auschwitz*
shmei raba	שְׁמֵהּ רַבָּא.	*Treblinka*
B'alma dibra kir'utei	בְּעָלְמָא, דִּי־בְרָא כִרְעוּתֵהּ,	*Majadanek*
ve-yamlikh mal-khutei	וְיַמְלִיךְ מַלְכוּתֵהּ.	*Belzec*
vejatzmach pirkuneh	וְיַצְמַח פּוּרְקָנֵהּ	*Sobibor*
vijekarev meshichei	וִיקָרֵב מְשִׁיחֵהּ	*Buchenwald*
bechajechon	בְּחַיֵּיכוֹן	*Dachau*
uvjomechon	וּבְיוֹמֵיכוֹן,	*Mauthausen*
be-hayei di-khol beit yisrael	וּבְחַיֵּי דְכָל בֵּית יִשְׂרָאֵל.	*Wilna*
ba-agala u-vizman kariv	בַּעֲגָלָא וּבִזְמַן קָרִיב,	*Ponary*
v'imru amen	וְאָמְרוּ אָמֵן:	*Chelmno*
Ye-hei shmei raba mevo-rakh	יְהֵא שְׁמֵהּ רַבָּא מְבָרַךְ,	*Oranienburg*
l'alam ul'almei 'almaya	לְעָלַם וּלְעָלְמֵי עָלְמַיָּא:	*Warsaw*
Yit-barakh ve-yish-tabah	יִתְבָּרַךְ וְיִשְׁתַּבַּח	*Bialystock*
Ve-yit-pa'ar ve-yitromam	וְיִתְפָּאַר וְיִתְרוֹמַם,	*Lwow*
Ve-yitnasei ve-yithadar	וְיִתְנַשֵּׂא, וְיִתְהַדָּר,	*Kielce*
Ve-yit'aleh ve-yit-hala	וְיִתְעַלֶּה, וְיִתְהַלָּל,	*Radom*
Shmei di-kudsha brikh hu	שְׁמֵהּ דְּקֻדְשָׁא. בְּרִיךְ הוּא	*Bochnia*
L'eila l'eila	לְעֵלָּא וּלְעֵלָּא)	*Tarnow*
Mikol bir-khata ve-shirata	מִן כָּל בִּרְכָתָא וְשִׁירָתָא,	*Krakow*
Tish-be-hata ve-nehe-mato	תֻּשְׁבְּחָתָא וְנֶחֱמָתָא	*Tarnopol*
Da-amiran b'alma	דַּאֲמִירָן בְּעָלְמָא,	*Dora*
v-imru amen	וְאָמְרוּ אָמֵן:	*Nordhausen*
Ye-hei Shlama raba	יְהֵא שְׁלָמָא רַבָּא	*Riga*
Min shmaya	מִן שְׁמַיָּא	*Kiev*
v-hayim tovim aleinu	וְחַיִּים טוֹבִים עָלֵינוּ	*Odessa*
v'al kol yisrael	וְעַל כָּל יִשְׂרָאֵל,	*Rumvuli*
v'imru amen	וְאָמְרוּ אָמֵן:	*Kamenec Podolsk*
Oseh shalom bimromav	עֹשֶׂה שָׁלוֹם בִּמְרוֹמָיו,	*(my village) Zabrod*
Hu ya'aseh shalom aleinu	הוּא יַעֲשֶׂה שָׁלוֹם, עָלֵינוּ	*All the other towns*
V'al kol yisrael	וְעַל כָּל יִשְׂרָאֵל,	*and villages may*
V'imru amen	וְאָמְרוּ אָמֵן:	*they all rest in peace*

130